HARBERT'S NEWS
FROM DUMPTON

HARBERT'S NEWS
FROM DUMPTON

Maurice Woods

Harbert's News from Dumpton

First published in Norwich Mercury weekly series
Copyright © Archant

Copyright this edition © Mousehold Press 2018

Mousehold Press,
6, Constitution Opening,
Norwich,
NR3 4BD

www.mousehold-press.co.uk

ISBN 978-1-874739-84-5

Cover design - Sue Mullard

Printed by PageBros., Norwich

Maurice Woods 1916-2015

Introduction

An old man propped up in his wheelchair on cushions of memories hardly seemed the most likely candidate to provide an impromptu cabaret treat for an impressive city event. Indeed, Maurice Woods seemed reluctant to go anywhere near a spotlight despite his "guest of honour" role at the launch of my dialect anthology, *Come Yew On, Tergether!*, at the Jarrold store in Norwich on a nippy November evening in 2011.

He was there to help mark my bringing together for the first time a host of local dialect enthusiasts and experts who have committed their passion to print. Maurice, former London editor of the *Eastern Daily Press* earned his chapter in the book as creator and long-time craftsman behind "Harbert's News from Dumpton". This weekly salute to a vibrant vernacular and special brand of Norfolk humour became a labour of love in the *Norwich Mercury Series* of weekly newspapers for the best part of 40 years. The first report from "a special correspondent" appeared in October, 1951.

Maurice now kept his powder dry until serious launching formalities had been sorted. Then he accepted a call to mardle, dipped deep into his Dumpton well and thrilled us all with a stop-press bulletin full of rustic revelry. The decades rolled away as a 95-year-old master of meaningful mirth put a memorable seal on a night of Norfolk pride and tradition.

It must have been the final public performance in the long and distinguished career of an outstanding journalist, gifted after-dinner speaker and important contributor to the Norfolk dialect preservation cause. Even so, it carried ample joy and laughter to convince me and Mousehold Press publisher Adrian Bell that Harbert was overdue his spot in the publication sun.

Maurice had mentioned to me "an old urge" to get a book of selected Harbert's bulletins published when I got in touch for a personal potted history and permission to feature a couple of longer instalments in *Come Yew On, Tergether!* There had been many requests for such a book over the years, he added.

"What has restrained me hitherto has been the sheer labour of retyping the whole lot. I have also been put off by the feeling that many of the words I use are no longer understood." Still, it would be a gift to posterity, mused Maurice in that telling epistle penned deep into his retirement at Tithe Farm, Ilketshall St. Andrew, near Beccles.

Yes, a tricky task to gain access to so many rural reports and then be presumptuous enough to pick just a few to illustrate a rare talent at work over such a long period. I knew just the man for such a marathon ... and the bells now ring out in celebration as Harbert's News From Dumpton bids to book a place among homely headliners on Norfolk's top shelf!

The road to Dumpton and district, teeming with endearing characters full of mischief-making antics and rustic repartee, started in the small Suffolk coastal village of Corton, three miles north of Lowestoft. That's where Maurice Woods was born in the middle of the First World War. He learned to speak the local dialect fluently as a lad growing up among old men "half of whom were fishermen and the other half farm labourers".

As a schoolboy, Maurice used to earn a bit of pocket-money by telling East Anglian yarns at bowls club dinners and the like. Clearly, that's where his taste for public speaking with a proud local flavour developed.

Early press reporting stints in Lowestoft and Dereham brought regular contact with colourful characters on rural district councils, at magistrates' courts, both on and in front of the bench, and other lively gatherings with that distinctive familiar flavour.

So, plenty of raw material at hand when Maurice started writing in dialect, more by accident than design in 1951. Bert Holroyd, editor of the *Norwich Mercury Series* of weekly newspapers asked him if he knew anyone who could pen him a dialect feature to match the popularity of the well-established Boy John Letters in the *Eastern Daily Press*. "I'll write it myself" replied Maurice.

"He was extremely dubious but let me have a trial run" he told me. The result was News from Dumpton provided by a rural sage and scribe called Harbert. He kept readers delightfully up to date for almost 40 years with about 1900 episodes to his name.

Inevitably, close comparisons were made between Boy John and Harbert, a habit bound to be revived by this eagerly-awaited volume. Well, one begat the other in many ways and both shared a deep passions for a rich dialect, "dew diffrunt" humour and close bonds embracing local communities. Even so, they were created by sharply contrasting characters. Sidney Grapes, who posted his first Boy John epistle to the

EDP in the austerity gloom of 1946, had served a long apprenticeship as a Norfolk comedian before combining his entertainment rounds with the written word. He lived and worked among the sort of folk he characterised in print for a dozen years until his death in 1958. Son of the village carpenter, he built up his Potter Heigham garage at the heart of Broadland into a thriving business where banter over bikes and motors nurtured his creative juices. His letters were contributed on an intermittent basis, more geared to the rhythms of changing seasons and popular village events like garden fete, harvest festival and a Norfolk Show outing rather than a regular weekly date.

Maurice Woods, whose newspaper years included a spell on the *Manchester Guardian*, was lured back home to serve as the *EDP* London editor, a post he filled for 25 years. He became Chairman of the Parliamentary Press Gallery, Chairman of the Newspaper Conference and Chairman of the Association of European Journalists. He also answered the proud call from Brussels to receive the European Prize for Journalism.

Perhaps he found much-needed relaxation as Harbert the rustic scribe after the pressures of keeping up with life along the corridors of political intrigue at Westminster. Maybe country characters like Billy "More-or Less" Hooper, Ow Bob Blewitt, Bumble the policeman and Gal Alice came as refreshing changes after interviews with the likes of Enoch Powell, Harold Wilson, Ted Heath and Margaret Thatcher.

In any case, it is clear Maurice put as much effort and time into his dialect offerings as any parliamentary report or *EDP* editorial column. Despite later mourning the sad decline of a truly local sound and vocabulary and bemoaning how many old stagers (like me) were forced to become bilingual, he cherished remnants of a glorious language and way of life.

For those unfamiliar with Norfolk dialect and little tricks it loves to play, let me stress it's well worth taking on the challenges playfully posed by Boy John, Harbert and countless others. There are no set rules in writing it down and that allows plenty of scope for rogue spellings and individual idiosyncrasies .

For example, the word "worse "can come out in several guises with "wass", wuss" and "warss" leading the pack. Some writers enjoy running a few words into each other – "betterannerhebbin" is opposite to "wassanwotterwuz" – and both begin to make sense when you say them slowly out loud.

Best general advice is to persevere and go with the flow. Or find a gnarled native and request a personal hearing. Tell 'em Harbert sent you … from the Dumpton College of Further Norfolk Education.

Keith Skipper,

Cromer, 2018

Maurice Woods and Keith Skipper, November 2011

Maurice Woods:

A natural writer and a leading authority on Norfolk dialect

Maurice Woods was born, I suspect, with a pen in his hand. He was a natural writer, and maybe there was a genetic element in his talent. His middle name, Sewell, was a nod to a family link with the author of *Black Beauty*.

He was born and raised, moreover, in Corton – right next to David Copperfield's Blundeston. And in the 40-plus years that I knew him I was often tempted to think that something of the genius of Dickens had passed on to Maurice.

He had a great way with words. As the London editor of the *Eastern Daily Press* from 1965 to 1980, he was the paper's main leader-writer, and I have never forgotten his beginning an editorial one day in the early-1970s in this fashion: "Enoch Powell is often applauded for saying what he thinks. He cannot be praised, of course, for thinking what he says." Given that Mr Powell had developed a substantial following because of his views on immigration, this would have been regarded as highly provocative by a good many *EDP* readers. But that didn't trouble Maurice in the slightest.

He thought – and rightly so – that an editorial should say what the paper believed to be right rather than what it knew to be popular. I should add that the Powell editorial went on for about 500 words; they were longer in those days. But in a way, everything that followed was superfluous. Maurice had said it all in one brilliant, crushing sentence.

He was a great pricker of heavily inflated balloons. Be you ever so high and mighty at Westminster or elsewhere, he would bring you back to the ground if he thought it desirable.

On one occasion in the 1960s when he was chairman of the Labour and Industrial Correspondents' group in Fleet Street, he had to respond to a speech by an employer's leader that had been full of complaints about Press coverage.

He noted that the previous speaker had made a Spooner-ism (in which he had referred to the 'Taily Delegraph'). And he continued: "I'm very aware of the danger of doing the same thing myself. So I won't describe Mr .... as a shining wit."

When he moved on to Westminster in 1965 as the *EDP*'s London editor, he was able to direct the same sharp critical talent at politicians. But it was generally done in a subtle manner, and he kept on good terms with virtually all of them. He liked both Harold Wilson and Ted Heath, and was even able to engage the latter in small-talk, which was not easily achieved. Towards the end of his career he also proved capable of getting Margaret Thatcher to laugh at herself, and that wasn't easily achieved either. He got on especially well with Lord (Jim) Prior.

In 1972 he became the chairman of the Parliamentary Press gallery, and in that role was able to use his outstanding talents as an after-lunch/dinner speaker. Even when the guest speaker was a leading politician, Maurice tended to be the star performer.

Where did Maurice stand politically? He was liberal-minded, but with a small 'l'. He didn't have any strong party leanings, but did possess firm views on certain issues. On Europe, for example. He was very much committed to European integration, and for many years held the chairmanship of the British section of the Association of European Journalists. He was also a robust advocate of nuclear energy. And it occurred to me that he had shown the courage of his convictions when he retired and chose to live just a few miles from Sizewell.

I had worked for the *EDP* for three years when I first met Maurice. By then I knew very well that he was a revered figure on the paper. And soon after joining his team in London as the paper's Labour and Industrial correspondent, I came to realise that his reputation for sagacity was thoroughly deserved.

Pearls of wisdom were frequently passed on by 'the master'. They included the advice that journalistically the future is always more important than the past. In other words, in writing about what had happened, one should always seek to pitch the story forward to what would happen next. Or might happen – giving one the opportunity to speculate. It seems so obvious; but it hadn't previously occurred to me.

Maurice wasn't born to wealth when he arrived in 1916; he was self-made, with an insatiable appetite for knowledge and life propelling him forward. This is a man who in his teens would cycle from Lowestoft to London (and back) to watch the ballet, and who didn't seem to understand why I found that remarkable. His first ever meeting, moreover, with Stanley Bagshaw – who many years later became editor-in-chief of

Eastern Counties Newspapers – was when they were both attending Russian lessons in Yarmouth. .

After serving in the second world war in the Royal Army Medical Corps, Maurice was appointed the editor of the *Dereham and Fakenham Times* in 1948, and I loved the tales he told of his time there. He must have been such a breath of fresh air in a stuffy and hierarchical small town community.

The local vicar considered himself to be very grand and insisted on addressing Maurice as "Woods" until Maurice replied in kind one day. The stunned silence was prolonged and deafening. There was a similar occurrence when Maurice had the nerve to say "I disagree" after the chairman of the local Rotary had pronounced on an issue of the day. No-one had ever disagreed publicly with this local grandee before, and Maurice found himself in the middle of a scene of widemouthed shock akin to a Bateman cartoon.

In his long career, the nearest he ever came to being sued was after he had filed a report for the *Pink 'Un* on a Dereham football match. The local team had played terribly in the first-half, and well in the second. Whatever had brought about this transformation, "it wasn't the strength of the tea served at half-team" quipped Maurice. But the person responsible for the teas took great umbrage.

Maurice was very proud of his East Anglian roots, and was a leading authority on the Norfolk dialect – as he showed in his 'News from Dumpton' columns, featuring Harbert, that were carried by the *Norwich Mercury* weekly papers. He took as much care and pride in composing these as he did in his reports from Westminster and his leader-writing.

When I last saw Maurice, in the nursing home in Beccles where he spent his last months, the flesh was very weak but his mind and spirit were still good. He was keen to give me the benefit of his views on political matters from the 1960s onwards.

I was sad that his body was giving up, but glad that he had lived so long. Surprised too, for in his younger days he had looked older than he was – he was mistaken for his own father when he first had a job interview with Eastern Counties Newspapers – and had never appeared to be very well; there was sometimes a grey-ish hue to his skin. For much of his working life, furthermore, he had insisted on smoking an old pipe that filled his office with fog.

Maurice was my journalistic mentor and I regard him as not just a source of great inspiration but a hero. He was very much a one-off, and it was a huge privilege to know him.

Chris Fisher, former London editor, *Eastern Daily Press*

Chris Fisher

Publishers' acknowledgements:

First we need first to thank Archant for kindly giving us permission to reproduce a selection from Maurice Woods' legacy of Harbert's News from Dumpton. We have also received welcome encouragement from Peter Waters, one-time editor of the *Eastern Daily Press*, and from its current editor, David Powles.
Thanks also are due to Rosemary Dixon, who is in charge of Archant's archive, for all her helpful advice.
Finally, we must express our appreciation to Helen Twigg and Nicholl Hardwick for their invaluable work in helping us make a varied selection from the hundreds of dispatches that came from Dumpton over the years, and for the laborious task of retyping them. And if you think typing a script in Norfolk dialect is quick and easy because the spelling doesn't matter, we suggest you just try it.

News from Dumpton

*We have asked our correspondent at Dumpton to let us
know each week what is happening in his village.
Here is his first dispatch.   – Editor*

THIS 'ERE 'LECKSHUN

Larst Monda wen I come home arter harvest my Ma say to me, she say, "Harbert," she say, "there's a letter fer yew." That ent orften I git a letter, except I git one from my brother Dicka was in th' Air Force. This one come from some feller what call hisself tha Edditer, only I dornt know his name cos the way he writ it wor in a proper frap like what my line wor tha fust time I went a-feeshin. He say as how he want me to tell yew pearple what read his pearper orl about what go on at Dumpton. So howd yew hard, an if any on yer are skewlmarsters dornt yew tell me I carnt spell, du I'll arst yer how many on yer cud milk tha ow cow.

Well, fust that rained so we coun't git tha straw rearked now they're gorn to hev another 'leckshun. I can't see why they want to keep hevin on em, thet dornt fare to make no difference to nothen. As ow Bob Blewitt say in tha Fox larst night, thas six o' one and harf-a-hundredweight o' tha other.

"I reckon yew're seen a few 'leckshuns in yar time," I say to Ow Bob. "Thet I hev," he say, "and they git wars stead o' better. I use ter git a pint o' mild orf my marster to go an wote Consarvative, an then he use to tearke tha hull lot on us down to tha willage in th' ow cart. Wen we got down there he use to tearke us into the pub jest to remind us which o' them candy-deartes wor which, an then he use to go an wote hisself. Wen we got a bit dry we use to git another pint orf the Liberal eargent to go an wote Liberal, an then one on us use to tell the Consarvative eargent what the Liberal wore doin, an' he use to give us another pint apiece to mearke us change our minds agen. Thet wor a rum ow job in them days."

I arst Ow' Bob who he use to wote for arter orl thet but he say he never know, cos he coun't read.

Corse most on em wote Learbour round hare cos they belong to the Union. The Consarvative ent a bad feller thow. Larst time he come hare he come into tha Fox, an he never hed a lot to say fer hisself. My Ma say he's a good-looken feller as she's a-goin to wote for 'im. She say she dornt mind if tha Consarvatives win tha 'leckshun only she dornt want them Tories back.

HARBERT
5th October, 1951

THET FOOTBALL MATCH WOR
A RUM OW JOB

If you red wot I writ larst week yew must a bin suffin worried, cos I sed I reckoned I woun't git no tea a-Sunday on account o' thare bein' a row over tha harvest festival. Thet tarned out I got a bigger tea 'n wot I would a done, cos I wor in bed. Ah, thet I wor. I coun't walk. Thet wor thet footborl match o' the Saturday wot done it.

My Ma say tha harvest festival wor a treart considerin tha learte spring. Tha chapel pearple went to tha charch o' that mornin, an tha charch pearple went to tha chapel o' tha evenin. Thare worn't no trouble. They hed a big tea in tha parish room, and tha gull Alice come up an browt me a lump o' kearke. She's my gull, an we're a-goin to git married only she ent got har bottom dror togither yit.

Thet footborl match wor a rum ow job. Tha Dumpton Wanderers went to Diddlin' in tha Rewral District League Jewbilee Charity Cup. Thare a hully good side only them Diddlin' Yewnited are a dutty lot. Corse, I dorn't play, I go as loinsman.

Our marster he's orlright, he allers gi' us a lorry. Thass a good 'un – well thet must be a good 'un dew he woun't a kept it this larst thutty-odd yare. Thet got us harf way thare afore thet brook down. We hed to walk tha rest o' tha way, an time we'd got tha beasts orf tha medder tha match wor learte a-startin.

Diddlin' won tha toss, like they allers dew, an set us to play up tha hill. Tha boy Chaarlie, our centre-forward, he kicked tha borl an started to run, an my hart if he didn't pass tha borl as thet wor a-rollin down agen. I wearved my flag for orfside, but I reckon the ref must a swallered his whistle. I found out arterwards thet he hed a sister wot married a Diddlin' feller. Corse, they scored, an I kep a-wearvin' my flag, but they kep on a-scorin', so I say to Chaarlie, I say, "Yew'll ha' tha adwarntidge wen yew chearnge over."

Thet stood at fowerteen goals apiece wen tha whistle blew, so we hed to play extra time. Corse, thet wor getting' dark by then, as thass how I come to wrinch my foot. I went arter the borl wen one o' them dutty Diddlin' harf-backs got windy an kicked it orf tha island. I stuck my foot in a rabbit-hole wot I never see an come a cropper. At fust I thowt I'd fratchered it, but one of em sed thet wor only brook. Arter orl thet I'd only wrung it. We're still in tha cup thow cos some o' tha Diddlin' men got carried orf an we won by tha odd goal o' thutty-nine. Thet wor a better win than thet sound, tew, cos the gearme wor three parts done afore we found we'd left our outside-right behind.

I see tha Yewnion a got a raise for the learbourers, so I went to tha marster an arst im for it. He say, "Well Harbert, bor" he say, "I carnet gi' yew no more'n wot I dew. My Missus tearke orl wot I git."

"Well bor," I say, "dew yew gi' me yar Missuses then. I'll charnce it."

HARBERT
19th October, 1951

HARBERT'S VOTE

We're done it now. I dornt know wot we're done, cos tha results aren't out yit, but we're done it. Ow Bob Blewitt say we're got shot o' six-hunnerd-an-suffin fewls, an stuck in six-hunnerd-an-suffin bigger fewls. My Ma 'ont hev that. She reckon they carnt be bigger fewls 'n wot tha larst lot wor.

We hed to go down to tha skewl to wote. I come in on my way home from wark, an got orf my bike jest as a car pulled up. My hart alive if my Ma dint git out on it. Corse I might a known she wor a-goin to git a lift, cos larst week we hed tha Consarvative eargent round. My Ma told im she wore a-goin to wote Consarvative, an then she say she got a gastrick stummick. Thet come on suffin crewel o' Tharsdays, she say. I tell har she's like a lot more o' tha Dumpton wimmin. They arst for a lift wen thare's a 'lecshun on, cos thass tha only time they see tha inside o' a car.

I let my Ma git in and git out agen afore I went in, dew thare'd a bin a row. I ent a-goin to say who I wote for, coss thass secret, but my Ma dornt like im. She say pollaticks ought to be left to them wot know suffin about it, an she reckon im wot I wote for dornt know narthin about anything. I say thass better'n knowin tew much about nartin, like some on em.

Wen I got inside tha skewl I see tha skewlmistress a-settin thare a-writin suffin on one o' them forms. She gi' me a look, an I give har one, but I never say narthin. I thowt I'd sin tha larst o'har twetty-odd yare ago wen I left skewl, but she allers tearke charge wen thare's a 'lecshun. I never did like har cos she's stingy.

I put my crorss on tha pearper, an then tha Wicar come in. Dew yew know our Wicar? He ent as sorft as some on em, thow he dussn't go nare tha Fox. He live in a duzzy grearte Wicaridge big enough for a warkhouse, but thare's only im an is missus an har sister. "Well, Harbert," he say, "exercisin yar dew right as a free sittizen?" "I dornt know about thet," I say. "I come hare to wote." Yew dornt know wot he's a-torkin about harf tha time.

We orl went down to tha Fox an lissened to tha wireless to see if we cud hare anything about tha results. Wen I got thare tha boy Chaarlie, wass our centre-forrard o' Saturdays, wor heving a argument wi' Tom Drew, the landlord. "They'll git in this time without no trouble," say Tom. "If they dew," say Chaarlie, "thare'll be thet much trouble arter-wards they'll git out agin."

Ow Bob Blewitt set thare by tha fire wi' his wropper round his neck, like he allers dew. They wor orl so busy a-arguin, no-one han't stood im a pint. I wet tha ow feller's whistle an arst im who he'd woted for. "I put a crorss alongside both on em," he say. "Tha two on em together 'ont meark more'n one Member o' Parlyment." I dornt know as how he ent right.

HARBERT
26th October, 1951

TRIP TO NORWICH

I're took tha gull Alice up to Norwich to see tha shops. Thet wor a proper good day's outin. We're lucky, we are, at Dumpton, cos thass easy enough gittin to Norwich. We're only got to cycle six mile to Flitmarsh an then thare's a bus go tha rest o' tha way. Thass a wonder more pearple dornt go. My Ma ent never bin to Norwich no more'n once an thet wor when my pore ow farther got took to horspital.

Dumpton pearple ent much for travellin. They dornt never go nowhere ceptin for tha shows. Some on em a bin as far as Kearmbridge, but they ent bin no fudder. Ow Bob Blewitt, he yewse to be a shepherd an he wor a-tellin on us abowt how he yewse to go down by train wi' a flock to Ipswich in tha ow days. Tha fust time he went, he say, he din't like tha way tha fellers on tha railway kep arstin im whare he wor a-goin. Tha marster hed bowt 'im a ticket, but they woun't let 'im git on tha train till they'd sin it. Then one on 'em say, "Yar a-goin to Ipswich ent yer?" an Ow Bob say, "Thass my business." Then they arst 'im what time he wor a-comin back. "Yew want to know a lot, dorn't yer," say Ow Bob. He orfen larf about it now in tha Fox, but o' corse in them days they dint know much about travellin.

Thet wor fine but windy tha mornin me and tha gull Alice staarted out for Norwich. I met har tha other end o' tha willage parst tha blacksmith's shop, an we walked for a bit afore I stuck har on tha bar an rid orf. We hed to dew thet cos Bumble, tha policeman, wor in his front gaarden an if he see tew on yer on a bike he git riled. She stuck har hid on my showlder an duzzy nare hed me orf tree or fower times. But we got to Flitmarsh orlright an left tha bike at th Duck an Drearke.

I wor glad when we got to Norwich cos I dornt like ow buses. Thet wor nare dinner-time, so we went in a posh plearce an hed some fish-an-chips. Thet wor werra nice in thare; the gull what sarved us wor werra friendly, an called me 'ow dare' an yew cud tearke as much winnygar as yew wanted out o' a duzzy grearte bottle. Then we went round tha shops. Tha gull Alice hed set har hart on gittin some stuff what they call taffiter to mearke harself a dress to go to tha whist-drives in. She say she wanted a nice bright red, but thet fared as if tha shops hent got none har colour. She kep a-mearkin on em tearke it down orf tha shelves an put it orl back agin, an kep a-sayin thet wor neither one thing nor tha other. Thet orl looked tha searme to me. I dornt know narthin about clorth, ceptin callyco, what my Ma's allers a-talkin about.

My hart, if I dint feel a proper fewl a-standin thare in them shops full o' wimmen, specially them ones what hev waxwarks orl over tha plearce wi' narthin on but their undercloes. "Keep yew yar eyes orf them," tha gull Alice kep a-sayin, as if I hent come thar in tha fust plearce to please har. I wanted to go an see tha beasts on tha maarket, but she woun't hev thet till she'd got har clorth. An then by tha time she'd got a bit to har likin thet wor time to be a-gittin back, an we dint know whare we wor. Thet took us tha best part o' an hour-an-a-harf to find tha bus stop agin. Anyhow, we got back orlright, only thet wor suffin frorsty by then an tha gull Alice say tha bar on my bike wor hully cold.

I'm a-lookin forrard to seein har in har new dress, an while I wor at it I got a wropper for pore ow Hezekiah, har granfar. Pore ow chap, I dornt reckon he'll larst a lot beyond Chrissmas.

HARBERT
14th December, 1951

MY HART ALIVE!

Me, I dornt believe in ghoosts. But thare's them at Dumpton as dew. Thare's that Jimma Fidgett, what fell inter tha hoss pond tha night he got chearsed by a feller wi' no hid. O' corse, he's harf sorft. Then thare's Ow Bob Blewitt...

I dorn't know what to mearke o' Ow Bob. I'll say this for 'im, he woun't tell yer no lie. Yet that there tearle o' his he wor a-tellin on us in tha Fox tearke some swallerin'. I'll tell it to yer searme as he told it to us, an' yer can say what yer like about it arterwards.

He wor a-settin' thare by tha fire like he allers do, wi' his ow wropper round his neck and werra nare harf a ounce o' my shag in 'is pipe. Thet wor Tom Drew, the landlord, what started 'im orf. Thare wor a gearle o' wind a-blowin', an tha ow sign wor a-creakin' outside, an' Tom say thet wor a night fit to wearke the dead in tha charchyard. "Some on em woun't tearke much wearkin," say Ow Bob, an gi' Tom such a look he dropped a harf o bitter on tha floor. "What a yew gorn light, Bob?" say Tom. "No, thet I ent," say Bob; "I wook one on 'em once.'

* * *

Well, bor, yew cud a hud a crab-apple drop orf a tree a mile away. We wor thet flummoxed none on us spook. In tha finish Ow Bob drearned is glarss, spit in tha fire an' told 'is tearle. "I wor sexton in them days," he say. "An a rum ow job it wor. Thet wor afore they added a bit to tha charchyard an they'd bin a-buryin' on 'em thet long thare worn't enough ground left to put a spearde in. I reckon thet'd be about a week afore Chrissmas I hed to dig a hole for pore ow John Potter, Humpty's granfar, what died o' tha pewmonia. I ent a-goin' to say how he got it. I went down thare o' tha Saturda' mornin' – he wor to be buried o' tha Monda' – and tha ground wor thet hard wi' frorst yew coun't shift it. I stuck at it orl day, but by tha time tea-time come thet worn't a quarter done. Thet wor tha searme o' that Sunda' an then, jest arter dinner, thet staarted to thaw. Time thet wor daark tha mowld wor soft enough to tarn, an' I reckoned if I took a lantern I could get ow John's grearve done afore thet froze agin.

"Thass several yare ago, an' if I hent bin a young 'un I might a known better. But I dint think narthin on it as I come trew tha charchyard gearte, an the light from tha lantern lit up orl them grearve-stones, an tha ow scritch owls wor a-hootin' round tha church steeple. I found John's grearve whare I'd left orf, stuck tha lantern on a heap o' mowld, an' got down an' staarted to dig.

"I'd bin a-diggin' about an hour or more when I felt tha spearde hit inter what I thort wor a lot o' stones. I got tha lantern to have a pearke at it, an' my hart, if thet worn't a skellyten lay thar. Thet proper put the wind up me at fust, an' then I got sort o' riled. If I slung it out I coun't get rid on it, an' if I left it be I shud hev to do orl thet diggin' agin. I'm tellin' yer, I wor a young un, an' thet ent as if young 'uns hev a proper respeck for tha dead.

* * *

"Tha long an' tha short on it is I staarted to cuss, an' tha more I cussed, tha more riled I got. In tha finish I kicked inter its skull wi' my bewte an' sung out, 'Yew duzzy grearte fewl, gittin' in my way. Wearke yew up an' sling yar hook., dew I 'ont get this har grearve done for Ow John's fewneral.'

"My Hart alive, if thet thare skellyton dint sit up! An' thass as true as I'm a-settin' hare – thet spook."

Ow Bob took a pull at 'is pint. "What did thet say, Bob?" arst Tom Drew. "Thet say," went on Ow Bob. "Thet say, 'Whass this tha Judgment Day?'"

"An' what did yew say, Bob?" arst Tom. "I jest stood thare," said Bob. "I wor thet flummoxed. An' then I say tha fust thing thet come inter my hid. I say, 'No thet it ent. Thass tha Thud Sunday in Adwent.'"

We orl larfed. "Thet worn't narthin to larf at," say Bob. "Thet thare skellyton got up on its tew feet – an' staarted to mob me suffin crewel."

"An' then thet done a dance, I spose," say tha Boy Chaarlie.

"Who's a-tellin' this tearle, yew or me?" say Ow Bob. "I stood thar wi' my hair on end an' its teeth kep a-champin' up an' down an thet kep a-proddin' on me in tha chest wi' its finger, an' I cud feel it trew my weskit like an icicle. An' evera time thet wearved its arms thet sounded like a boy runnin' a stick along a fence.

"Thet run on about me a-wearkin' on it afore the Judment Day, an' say if I dint put it back comfortable – like I found it – thet'd ha' me alongside it to keep it company. An' then thet staarted a-lookin' round as if thet'd lorst suffin. Them tew grearte black holes in its skull went this way an' thet way, an' in the finish thet say to me, 'What a yew done wi' my grearve-stone?'

"I opened my mouth but I never say narthin, cos my teeth staarted to chatter thet hard I bit my tongue. Tha skellyton caught hold o' my coat, mearde me pick up tha lantern, an' afore I could think what to dew we wor a-crawlin' round tha charchyard a-pearkin' at orl the grearve stones. Evera time thet see a nearme thet knew thet let out a shout. Thare wor one belongin' to a feller called Bloggs what tha skellyton say wor its cousin, an' when thet see 'Gorn to Glory' writ on tha stone thet werra nare larfed its skull orf. 'Thass the larst plearce ow Bloggs'd go,' thet say."

* * *

"I wor jest a-wonderin' how tha hoike I cud get away when tha skellyton hollered out, 'My hart alive!' Well, bor, I'd got over my fright a bit by then, an' I coun't help larfin, an once I staarted larfin I coun't stop. 'What tha hoike are yew a-larfin' at?' thet say, an' I say, 'Bor, yew hent got a hart, an' if yew hed, thet woun't be alive.' 'This hare ent narthin to larf at,' say tha skellyton. 'We're come round in a sarcle, an' this hare grearve next tha one what I come out of a got my nearme on it – an' my missuses.' Well, thet fared as if thet thare skellyton began to remember a bit about how they'd stuck his missus in alongside on 'im, an' he wor a-tryin' to remember a bit more, an I wor still a-larfin', when go to heck if tha grearve-stone dint fall over backwards an up come a skellyton harf as big agin as tha fust one."

* * *

"Bor, I're hud some mobbin' in my time, but I ent never hud no one mob like thet big skellyton mobbed thet little un. 'I hud yar woice,' thet say, 'an high time tew. I're bin a-wonderin' whare yew'd got tew this larst hunderd-an fifty-odd yare. Walkin' in yar sleep agin, I reckon, searme as yew used tew when yew an me lived in tha ow house next tha mill. An' whare did yew walk tew then? Arter them mawthers down tha dairy, as if I dint know what wor a-goin' on. I hent bin down hare no more'n a day afore yew come out o' yore coffin an' burrowed orf arter different company. Well, yew can jest come back whare yew belong, an' be quick about it...' An' so thet thare skellyton's misssus kep on at 'im warse an what my missus dew, an I stood thare a-larfin fit to drop. An' Mr. Skellyton wor thet scared o' Mrs. Skellyton he slung his arms round my neck an' hollered, "Keep har orf me!' an' I hung on tew him a-howlin' wi' larfin', an I cud see tha ow lantern a-shinin' trew his ribs."

"An' then, somehow," say Ow Bob, "I dorn't remember no more."

Without a ward of a lie, thare wornt none on us cud think of anythin' to say. An' then a woice say, "I're hud him tell that tearle afore." We tarned round, an' thare set Ow Dan Forster, what'd crept in while Bob wor a-talkin'. "What he never tell yer," say Dan, "is as how thet wor tha night we found him up agin tha charchyard fence, wi' his arms round tha palins, a-garpin trew it at 'is lantern what stood on tha other side. He wor a-larfin 'is hid orf orlright. But he allus put the blearme on tha wrong sort o' spirits. They worn't tha sort yew see, they wor tha sort yew smell. An' tha only mobbin' he hud thet night wor arter we'd took 'im home.'

Ow Bob spit in the fire agin, an give Dan a look. "I never had no spirits," he say. "Orl I hed wor ten pints o' mild. An come to think on it, orl I're had tonight is tew."

HARBERT
21st December, 1951

A POLICEMAN'S JOB

Larf! My hart, I duzzy nare barst tha other week when Bumble, thass our policeman, nabbed Humpty Potter. I coun't tell yer narthin about it at tha time cos Bumble say I mussn't. Not till arter thet hed bin in tha police-court, he say. Well, thet a bin in tha police-court now, so Bumble carnt stop me.

Y'see I wor a witness. I got a mornin out an fower bob, so I ent a-grumblin. Thet wor time somebodda got their hooks on to Humpty, an tha fust time I see Bumble I say to myself, I say, "Thet thare feller's tha one what'll dew it."

Thet fare is if Bumble'd been arter him ever since thet night larst October when we see tha Northern Lights. I reckon yew remember how Ow Bob Blewitt told 'im whare Humpty hed gorn, an Bumble went tha other way, thinkin thet wor a trick. Young Bumble wor suffin riled about thet, cos he're bin gettin a tidy few complearnts about pearple's pullets bein took, an he knew whare they wor a-goin.

I wor a-comin parst tha end o' tha Wicaridge Loke learte one night on my bike when I run inter Bumble. I put my front light on right quick, but Bumble never say narthin about thet bein orf. "Howd yew hard a minute ow partner," he say. "Humpty Potter's in thet thare wood an I'm a-goin to git 'im. Dew I go in tha wood an holler he'll come out trew thet gap in tha hidge. Then dew yew shine yar light on 'im. I'll hev 'im."

Well, bor, thass agin nearture to dew a thing like thet. None on us think a lot o' Humpty, but thet thare's a policeman's job. But afore I cud say yes or no Bumble wor a-kickin up a row back o' tha hidge, so I got on my bike an staarted orf down tha road. I might a stayed an done as he say, an I might not, but I never got tha charnce to mearke up my mind. I wor jest a-goin parst tha gap in tha hidge when Humpty come trew it like a shot outer a gun, an both on us ended up on tha floor wi' my bike round our nicks. "Yar a duzzy fewl, Humpty," I say, but I never say no more cos Bumble come out like a rocket an landed atop on us.

I hed to go to Flitmarsh o' Monda for tha police-court kearse. Tha magistreartes arst me some rum ow questions. They got some rum ow arnsers, tew. "Wuz this hare Potter in parsewt o' coneys?" say one on 'em. "No thet he wornt," I say. "He wor arter rabbits." Corse, he wor arter pheasants rarely. At any rearte, thare wor tew on em under my bike with 'im. I know, cos thet took me tha best part o' harf an hour to git tha glarss from my front light out on 'em. But thet dornt dew to tell them magistreartes tew much.

Mark yew, Humpty torked hisself out on it. He say he wor a-goin down tha road arter a wisit to 'is sick sister when Bumble fell atop on 'im. He say he coun't help it if a brearce o' pheasant wor a-walkin acrorst tha road when tha accident occarred. They give 'im what they call a on-condishunal discharge. But I hed to larf.

HARBERT
25th January, 1952

FER THA HULL LOT*

We hed to put our daarts club dinner orf. Well, we coun't a hed it larst week, could we? Thet woun't a looked right. Besides, thare wornt none of us in a mind for beer an pickles. Thet wor like when ow Hezekiah died, tha willage fared as if thet'd lorst somebodda we'd orl known a long time.

I wor a-torkin to Ow Bob Blewitt in tha Fox o' Friday night, and I wor a-sayin' how we orl stopped wark o' tha mornin when we hud tha fire alaarm go at Flitmaarsh. Thet wor a rummun, I say to Ow Bob how we dornt go a lot on thet sort o' thing aroun' hare, an yit this hare wor different. We orl stood thare, wi' our caps in our hans, an tha raggety ow flag wor a-flutterin at harf-marst over tha charch, an thass a fact, bor, I jest dornt know what to say about it.

Corse, Ow Bob he remember Queen Wictoria a-dyin, let alone orl tha Kings we're hed since har. "I never did go much on tha gentry, Harbert bor," he say to me. "Harf on em what calls thareselves tha gentry ent. Thet ent orfen yew come acrorst a proper gennleman, but when yew dew yew know it. Thare ent a lot on em left, but I reckon them what think thareselves gentry woun't dew no haarm to tearke a leaf out o' thare

---

* This would have been written a week after the death of King George VI.

27

book. An from what I're sin thare's pletty could larn a thing or tew from Royalty when it come to treartin pearple right."

I ent never thort a lot about it afore, but thaas right what he say. I wor arguin wi' a feller tha nexter mornin, an he say to me, "Harbert," he say, "thass a lot o' squit mearkin orl this to-dew. What a he ever done fer yew?" "Well," I say, "he ent never stood me a pint o' mild in tha Fox, but come to thet, what a yew ever done fer 'im? Thet ent a kearse o' 'im dewin suffin fer us an us dewing suffin fer 'im, thass a kearse o' orl on us dewin suffin fer tha hull lot on us," I say, "an he done a duzzy site more fer tha country'n what ever yew did, nor me neither."

I dornt know if yew can see what I mean, but thet come tew me in my hid, an I know what I'm a-gittin at, but carnt say it.

Our daarts club dinner, what we put orf, we hed larst night. Thare wor some what wanted to put it orf agin arter thet say in tha pearper thet tha Queen wanted dinners fer tha Guvenment, trearde, charity and the aarts to go on as yewsual. Tom Drew, tha landlord, he's tha secketery, he say thet hent got a lot to dew wi' tha Guvenment, but thet 'is trearde, some o' the profits go to charity, an thare ent a lot o' difference atween aarts and daarts. So we hed it. Tha Boy Chaarlie, what play centre-forrard few tha Wanderers, he got tha inderwidewal cup, an 'im sing a song. Thet wor a proper good dew.

Corse, tha next big dew'll be tha Footborl Club dinner, but we dornt hev thet till arter tha season. We allers staart thet orf wi' a gearme of bowels.

HARBERT
22nd February, 1952

JEWLIUS SEIZER'S PLEARTE

Well, together, how are yew a-gittin on wi' yar muck spreedin? We're nigh on done ours. We're done a bit o' plowing an orl – an thare's a rum ow tearle to tell about thet.

Tha marster wor a-dewin a bit hisself on tha trackter when he felt tha blearde catch on suffin, an up come a dutty ow tin plearte. Yew coun't see a lot for mowld an when we screarped it orf a bit thet woun't a lot better. "Whadda yew mearke o' thet, Harbert, bor?" say the marster. "Not a lot," I say, an no more I dint.

But when the marster took it hoom an cleaned it up proper thet fared to be silver, an thet hed a sort o' kind o' pattern on it. Thare wor a feller what fared to be a-running an he never hed narthin on exceptin a billycock hat without a brim, an' what looked like wings 'is feet. An then thare wor a mawther what I dussn't a-showed to tha gal Alice, cos she never hed narthin on neither, an she wor a-holding a grearte ow bunch of grearpes. An thare wor some funna sort o' writin on it.

"Tha best thing yew can dew is show thet thare to tha Wicar," I say. So I went down wi' tha marster to see tha Wicar, cos he know orl about them things. Thet dorn't matters what yew dig up around hare, tha Wicar can tell yer where thet come from. "Well," he say when he looked at it, "yew know what yew're found, dorn't yer? Yew're found a roamin dish."

I dint know what he meant at fust, till he staarted torkin about orl them roamin soldiers, like Jewlius Seizer an thet lot, what yewsed to come around hare a long time parst. "They got one o' their hellemets out o' tha river nare North Ellum," say tha Wicar, "an they keep a-digging their stuff up round Lynn way." Well, bor, thet fare as if thet thare ow dish might be warth suffin, which is orl tha marster wor bothered about. Only thet Wicar say they're gotta hev a hinkwest on it, wi' a corriner an orl, like thet wor a dead man. Thet sound a rummin to me.

We never did hev a hinkwest at Dumpton afore, only once, time ow Harra Frorst fell in tha Pike Drearn. They fished 'im out an browt tha wardict in accidental.

Still, thet seem a rummin to me they should hev a hinkwest on a bit of an ow plearte what some roamin soldier went an dropped, even if he'd hed a few tew many at that time like what pore ow Harra hed. I arst ow Bob Blewitt what he thowt about it. "Who'd yew say dropped it?" he say. "Jewlius Seizer," I say. "Thass afore my time," say Ow Bob.

HARBERT
19th September, 1952

29

THA PUBLICK'S MONNA

Thass like I told yer. They're a-goin to hold a hinkwest on thet thare silver plearte what tha marster plowed up on 'is land tha other week. I carnt see no sense in thet meself. Tha Wicar says thass a roamin dish what Jewlius Seizer or one o' his men must a dropped. I say to 'im, I say yew could hold fifta hinkwests without yew could give tha duzzy thing back to Jewlius Seizer.

Thet ent it, say tha Wicar, thet orl depend on whether thet wor put thare o' parpose, or whether thet come thare accidental. They're got to find thet out, he say. I carnt see as thet matters, I say, but if thet dew, I say, yew dornt need to wearst tha publick's monna on a hinkwest to find thet out. Thet stick out a mile, I say. Thet thare Jewlius Seizer, nor yit 'is men, woun't go puttin tha best Sunda silver in tha middle o' one o' tha marster's filds not unless they'd gorn light.

Me, I reckon thet must a bin dropped accidental, when Jewlius Seizer wor a-tearkin orl 'is walables orf to Norwich to rearse a bob or tew, like what my ow uncle did time thare wor orl thet thare onemployment. Searme thing happened ter 'im, a candle-stick warth harf-a-crown hopped out o' tha sack on tha back o' his bike, an he never did find it. Thow why Jewlius Seizer should a went acrorst tha marster's fild is a misstry to me, cos thet ent a short cut to nowhere.

Corse, thare a bin a lot o' furriners pearkin about on tha farm ever since we found thet thare plearte. To heck if I know where they orl come from, one on em wor a woman about six foot square what say she come from one o' them varsities. She allers did know, so she say, thet this hare willage wor a roamin camp.

"Then yew know more'n what we dew," I say, "an we're lived hare orl our lives." Thet shut har up.

Then thare wor another feller come down, proper city feller he wor, werra smart, an well built about tha showlders, only 'is hair wor a bit tew long for my likin. He come up to me an "Dew yew find any more o' them things," he say, "dorn't yew say narthin to tha marster. I'll gi' yew a good price for 'em."

"How much?" I say. "

"What about harf-a-quid?" he say.

"What about it?" I say.

"Think how much beer yew could git for harf-a-quid," he say.

"I dornt drink," I say.

"Listen, son," he say – thet got me riled for a staart, cos he wornt no older'n what I am – "I'd be dewin yew a fearvour givin yew harf-a-quid for suffin what ent no yewse to yew."

"Look yew hare, Dad," I say – thet got 'im on tha hop – "if thass warth harf-a-quid to yew, thass warth harf-a-quid to me."

"What could yew dew with one o' them things?" he say.

"Searme as yew, I reckon," I told 'im. "We eat orf pleartes in tha country searme as what yew dew in tha town."

He slung 'is hook.

Then, o' course, tha marster's lawyer come to see 'im. I thowt he'd hev to hev a finger in it somewhere. Pinch, 'is nearme is, of Pinch, Pinch, Usher an Bunion, from Flitmarsh. Tha fust Pinch wor 'is father, what died an left 'im tha bizness, an by thet time Usher hed retired an bowt up Diddlin Hall, an Bunion hed went orf to live in Canada with 'is neffew. So this hare Pinch is tha only one left, an what with one thing an another I reckon he dew orlright. Yew know what tha marsters are – if somebodda sneeze over their land they run orf tew a lawyer.

HARBERT
26th September, 1952

SEIZED FOR THA CROWN

Yew remember thet thare silver plearte what tha marster found on 'is land? Well, my hart if they ent gorn an run orf with it. Seizin it for tha Crown, they call it. Thet ent what Ow Bob Blewitt called it in tha Fox larst night.

They hed tha hinkwest on it in tha Willage Hall o' Tewsda. Tha feller in charge wor him whass known as tha Corriner, thow Ow Bob Blewitt reckon he wor allers known as tha Crowner when he wor a young 'un. Then they hed a jewry what they reckoned wor twelve good men an true,

31

thow I dint know harf on em so I coun't say. They come from Flitmarsh as far as I could mearke out.

I see tha marster set thare lookin like he wor a-gorn to lay about 'im if they tried to diddle 'im, but he dint hev tew, cos tha Corriner put 'im right afore they'd hardly staarted. Thet dint seem right, say tha Corriner, as how when a feller found suffin they should tearke it orf 'im, but thare wornt narthin for 'im to worry about, cos he yewsually got paid for it jest tha searme. Tha marster fared a bit easier in 'is mind arter thet. To speak tha honest trewth, so did I, cos arter all I helped 'im find it, an I could dew with a couple o' new tires on my bike.

Well, arter tha marster hed said 'is bit about how he plowed it up, a totty little ow chap with glarsses tarned round an said he wor a narkalollajist or suffin, an he knew what thet thare plearte wor. Accordin to what he say, thet wor a roamin frewt dish what must a bin berried when times wor hard, like when my ow uncles berried tha best spewns to keep 'is relearshuns from layin hold on em when tha ow woman died. Like thet, he say, thet counted as treasure.

Tha jewry set thare lookin as thow thet mearde about as much sense to them as what thet did to me. So tha Corriner , a werra friendly sort o' feller what dint look as thow he spent harf 'is time garpin at corpses, he told thet thare jewry what he reckoned they ought to say, an what they dint ought to say. In tha finish they browt tha wardict in thet this plearte wor treasure, an thet'd hev to go to tha Crown. Tom Drew, tha landlord, he tarned round an give me a wink, an say, "Thet'd a bin better if they'd said tha Fox 'stead o' tha Crown "

I arst tha marster what he reckoned he'd git out of it, an he say his lawyer told him some London feller what see it reckoned thet wor warth tha best part o' fower or five hundred pound. I see Humpty Potter crowdin a barrer up our loke tha nexter mornin, so I told 'im. "My hart," he say, "tha times I're bin acrorst thet thare fild without knowin thare wor orl thet monna layin thare underfoot." Then a look come in 'is eye so I kep quiet. Thet wount surprise me none dew I wor to go up tha fild o' nights afore we git tha winter barley in, to see Humpty diggin away like a duzzy ow moll.

HARBERT
3rd October, 1952

DEWIN FOR HARSELF

Mrs Frorst, what live next door tew us, she're done for harself now. She're bin arstin for trouble ever since har pig knocked our fence down. Well, bor, dew she want trouble she can hev it.

Fust go orf she reckoned thet ent our fence, but hars, an thet wornt har pig what knocked it down but my little ow dorg. My Ma told har a thing or tew. "My pore ow husband stuck thet thare fence up when he wor alive," she say.

"So he may hev," say Mrs Frorst, "but thet wor my husband what employed him to dew it."

"Dornt talk so sorft," say my Ma; "yar husband never employed nobodda, an nobodda never employed him dew they could help it, tha drunken good-fer-narthin."

"Why yew foul-mouthed ow hag, yew," say Mrs Frorst. "I'll thank yew not to designate tha memory o' my pore husband."

"He never did hev no memory," say my Ma, "dew he'd a remembered tha one pound ten what he borrered orf o' my husband tha night o' tha armistice in tha fust warld war."

* * *

Corse, Mrs. Frorst is like thet thare. Dew she can git suffin for narthin she's arter it like a dorg arter a rabbit. She never did hev a day's illness in har life till tha Nashunal Health come in, an since then she're hed one thing arter another. When har fowls caught tha croup she staarted to corf suffin crewel so as she could git some physick to stick in their mash. I never dew know whether they're har own eyes or glass ones, an thass my belief she'd cut har leg orf an arst for a wooden one dew she wor to run short of a copper stick. She got harself a new set o' teeth jest afore Chrissmas, about tha time she wanted to kill thet thare pig, an they dew say she sent tha form for killin tha pig to tha Nashunal Health an tha one for tha teeth to tha pig marketin board. My Ma reckon thass a pity they dint kill har an give tha teeth to tha pig.

Howsomever, about this hare fence. Mrs Frorst reckon thet wornt har pig what knocked it down cos thet hent never bin out o' tha sty, but she hed to chearnge har tewne arter Humpty Potter told me he ketched thet thare pig harfway down tha loke tha searme Sunda mornin as what tha fence fell down. Then she come hollerin to my Ma about thet bein har fence an she wor a-goin to hev us in court for damidges. "Dew thass yar fence," say my Ma, "thass yar plearce to put it up agin, an dew thass ours, then I'll see yew dew put it up."

"Alright," say Mrs Frorst, "I'll hev it put up an I'll send yew tha bill."

"Best thing yew can dew," say my Ma, "is sell yar pig to pay for it."

"You leave my pig alone," say Mrs. Frorst; "even if thet did knock tha fence down – an I ent sayin thet did – thet wor yar dorg come chearsin it round my yard knockin my brockerlo down what mearde it dew it."

* * *

Well, this went on all trew Chrissmas until in tha finish she staarted puttin it up larst week. Thet wor only a matter of a few poosts brook orf trew bein rotten, an all thet wanted wor some new uns put in. I come hoom Saturda an found Fred Johnson, whass a carpenter, diggin holls for em.

"Whare tha hoike dew yew think yew're a-diggin them holls, bor?" I arst. Without a ward of a lie, they wor a foot or more on tew our land.

"I'm a-diggin on em whare Mrs. Frorst told me," say Fred.

"We'll see about thet," I say.

Corse, I up an see Mrs Frorst.

"Fred Johnson's puttin them poosts in their rightful plearce," she say. "When my pore husband give yar father good money to put thet fence up he put it tew far our way. He allers wor a bit thick in tha skull an thet wornt no good us a-tellin on him, so we let it lay. But thass being put right now, an yew can holler as loud as yew like."

Well, she're done for harself. I'm a-goin to see Lawyer Pinch in tha mornin.

HARBERT
22nd January, 1954

34

THASS ALL MOONSHINE

"Thet say hare they'll be gittin to tha moon in twenty or thutty yares' time," say Fred Johnson, what wor readin tha pearper alongside tha fire in tha Fox.

"Who will?" say Ow Bob Blewitt.

"Yew ont," say tha boy Fred.

"Ont what?" arst Ow Bob.

"Git to tha moon," say Fred.

"No, thet I ont," say Ow Bob, "thass a lot o' squit, thass what thet is."

"I dorn't know so much," say Fred, "what with them at-em bombs an one thing an another, thass a rummun what they can think of, ent it?"

"They woun't never git em orf o' tha ground," say Ow Bob, "an if they did they woun't never come down agin."

"Whass to stop em?" say Fred.

"They woun't be allowed tew," say Ow Bob, "thet'd be goin agin tha Bible. Dew tha Lord hed a meant yew to fly to tha moon He'd a give yew wings."

"An dew He'd a meant yew to wear trousers yew'd a bin born with em on," say Fred.

"Yew young 'uns ent got no respeck for us old 'uns no more," say Ow Bob. "Thet wor diffrent in my time. Thass all these hare plearnes an speedways what never should a bin inwented whass a-puttin wrong ideas inter pearple's hids."

* * *

Jest then Slim McGinty, one o' them Yanks what live in tha Manner House whare pore ow Major Mott yewsed to be, he come in all of a spuffle. "Give us a hand quick," he say.

Well, bor, thet wor a stingy ow night outside, an Slim fared to a got his missis in a proper fix. Yew know how tha Pike Drearn overflow acrorst tha rood? Well, thare must a bin a foot or more o' water in thet thare dip on tha Flitmarsh rood, an then with all this hare frorst thet frooze over solid. Slim, he're bin out furrin for a bit and he never knew narthin about this hare. He wore a-nippin along in his greart ow yeller car, with his missis along on him, an down he come on to this hare ice afore he see it. Corse, thet'd a bin bad enough dew thet'd bin narthin but water, but bein as how thet wor ice tha ow car slewed round an sailed soshways orf o' tha rood an finished up in tha middle o' tha Pike Drearn. Thare it lay, with tha back end on it trew tha ice an tha front end stickin out, an thare worn't narthin he could dew. Well, he crawled out hisself an splodded trew tha sluss to tha edge o' tha deek, but he hed to leave his missis inside. Then he run up to tha Fox.

* * *

We got tha marster's lorry out for a staart, run it down tha hill to git it goin, hotted it up a bit, an then went orf to see what we could dew. We got a rope hitched to tha car, but tha ow lorry-wheels jest went round an round on tha ice an never got nowhare. In tha finish Fred Johnson an tha boy Chaarlie give Slim a hand to carry his missis ashore, an Tom Drew took har orf up to tha Fox for a bottle o' stout and a warm.

Then we imitearted to git a trackter tew it, but thet wornt no good cos tha engine wor frooze up an I go to heck if we could git it staarted. In tha finish Enoch Fletcher say, "What yew want is a good hoss," he say. "Thare's suffin in thet," I say, an I drawed on to tha marster's an got hold o' Prince. "Tha thing on it is," say Enoch Fletcher, "they hent got no wheels to slip." Well, thass right enough, ent it? We got Prince hitched to thet thare car, an he pulled an he pulled an in tha finish he give one grunt an thet thare car come crackin trew tha ice an on to tha rood.

* * *

Time we got back to tha Fox, Ow Bob Blewitt still set thare by tha fire.
"Flyin to tha moon," he say, "thass a lot o' squit."
"Who say so?" say Fred Johnson.
"I say so," say Ow Bob. "Yew'll git about harfway thare an then yew'll git stuck, searme as thet thare Yanky feller in tha Pike Drearn. An then what'll yew dew? Yew'll come runnin hoom for a hoss to pull yew out."

HARBERT
5th February, 1954

FOLLERING FOOTPRINTS

Them thare kids from tha Fen Cottages – proper lot o' little warmints they are – they're bin a-goin wild with all this snow about. Bumble, our policeman, he's still imiteartin to find out which one on em hulled a snowball with a brick in it what knocked him orf o' his bike.

Thet Bartholomew Smith (him what married tha skewlmistress) he staarted tha Boy Scouts to keep em out o' mischief. Well, I ent sayin thet hant done a lot o' good, an then agin I ent sayin thet hev.

Tearke tha night tha snow come. Thet wor tha night o' tha Boy Scouts' meetin. Time they got to tha skewl, everawhare wor white. Corse, thet Bartholomew Smith, he hed to hev one o' his bright ideas. "I know," he say, "we'll go trackin."

"Whass thet?" say them kids.

"Thass to larn yew to yewse yar eyes," say Smith. "Yew give me ten minnits staart, an then yew tearke a lantern an foller my footprints in tha snow."

Thet jest suited them kids. He lit em a hurry-cane lamp, an then orf he went. They give him ten minnits staart, an then they sailed orf in tha other direckshun.

* * *

I never did find out whare Smith got tew. He spent about an hour a-going round an round a-wonderin why tha kids never caught him. But them kids hed a rare ow time. Young Jimma Forster, he's tha ringleeder, allers is, trust him.

"Right," he say, "tha Scout-marster want us to dew some trackin," he say, "well then, we'll dew some. Only thet ent no good a-follerin him, cos we know thass him all tha time. What we'd best dew is foller somebodda else's footprints an yew never know, we might ketch a bargler or suffin."

Well, bor, thet wornt long afore they got their ow glimmers on some footprints mearde by a feller in greart ow bewts with hobnails. They follered these hare footprints acrorst tha green, parst tha charch, an harfway up tha Wicaridge Loke. Then them footprints went trew a gap in tha hidge.

"Ah," say tha boy Jimma, "thass a bargler alright, I go to heck if it ent."

So all them Scouts they nipped trew tha hidge arter them footprints an rent a few holes in their garnseys inter tha bargain.

Arter they'd gorn in an out o' tha trees a bit, they hud a stick go crack ahid on em, an young Jimma mearde em stop.

"Thare he be," he say; "tha best thing we can dew is mearke a ring round him so he carnt git out."

So some went one way an some tha other, an young Jimma put tha lamp out so's tha feller woun't see em, an in tha finish they wor all a-spreedin theirselves out round whare this feller wor. Well, they wearted a bit but this feller never mearde no move, an thet wor gitting a bit stingy, so Jimma say to tha boy what wor with him, he say,

"Thare's only one thing to dew," he say, "thass what tha Red Injuns dew."

"Whass thet?" say tha other boy.

"Barn him out," say Jimma.

* * *

Mind yew, I reckon young Jimma done what he done for tha best. A younster what think he's ketchin barglers dornt stop to arst hisself which is tha right way an tha wrong way o' dewin it. Young Jimma splattered some o' tha parafeen outer thet thare lamp in a duzzy great ring all round whare them boys wor hidin, an then he set light tew it.

Fust I knew about it wor when we hud tha fire engine nippin trew tha willage, an we all rushed outer tha Fox to see what wor goin on. Somebodda reckoned harf o' Ephraim's wood wor alight, so orf we went to see tha fun. We got thare as sewn as what tha firemen did, an then we see them Boy Scouts a-settin on some feller on tha ground. "We're ketched a bargler," they hollered.

Only they hant. They'd ketched Humpty Potter, an he dint fare to be tew plearsed about it

HARBERT
12th February, 1954

SING-SONG FER THA WIRELESS

We see a wan marked "B.B.C." stand outside tha Wicaridge, thet'd be a week or tew since Enoch Fletcher say, "Whass tha matter with tha Flitmarsh bakery?"

"Whadda yew mean?" I arst.

"Why, tha Wicar a chearnged his baker by tha looks on it," he say. "Thet thare wan come from tha Beethoe Bakin Company, thet say so on tha side."

"Dornt talk so sorft," I say, "thass tha Bedstead Buildin Company, tha Wicar's gittin his chimney sin tew."

Thet tarned out we wor both on us wrong. Thet come from tha pearple what run tha wireless. Corse, we're hud them called tha B.B.C. afore, but thet never come inter our hids thet might be them in Dumpton. Howsomever, thass who they wor, an about time tew. I allers did say they oughter put Dumpton on tha wireless. Well, bor, they're bin back agin since then, an I reckon dew yew lissen hard enough yew might hare us one o' these hare days.

* * *

We dint know who tha feller wor when he come in tha Fox. All dressed up he wor, like he wor goin tew a fewneral. He stuck his elbow on tha counter an say to Tom Drew: "I'll hev a shabbily" (thass what thet sounded like).

"Thet yew on't," say Tom Drew, "cos I ent got none."

"Never mind," say this feller, "mearke it a shatto nerf" (I dornt know if thass right).

"What the hike is thet?" arst Tom Drew.

"Give me a beer," say this feller. I tell yer, them city fellers talk wet harf tha time.

Then he say tew us, "Dew any o' yew fellers play tha fiddle?" We garped at one another.

"Yew want to try Humpty Potter," say the boy Chaarlie, "he spend seven days a week on tha fiddle." We all larfed, but this feller dint fare to see what we wor a-larfin at.

"What I want," he say, "is a good rousin sing-song, with all tha old songs an someone accompanyin on a fiddle or suffin."

"Whass it for?" arst Tom Drew.

"Hant tha Wicar told yer?" say this feller. "Thas for tha B.B.C."

* * *

Well, o' corse, we parked up a bit then. "Yew mean tha wireless?" arst Ow Bob Blewitt.

"Ah," say this feller.

"Thare yew are," say Tom Drew, "thare's Ow Bob Blewitt, he'll give yew a tewne on his tin whissel."

"No fiddle?" say this feller.

"Thare's Mrs Higgins's dorter," say tha boy Chaarlie, "she're bin tearkin lessons."

"Thet ent quite tha sort o' thing," say tha wireless feller.

"She can play all tha way up tha scale an all tha way down agin," say tha boy Chaarlie.

"She ent narthin to tha gal Ada, Enoch Fletcher's niece," say Fred Johnson. "I're hud har play 'Tha Blewbells o' Scotland' on tha pianner without a note wrong."

"Thet ent what we're a-lookin for," say tha wireless feller.

"We hed a brass band hare several yare ago," say Ow Bob Blewitt, "but thet fearded away."

"Thare y'are," say Tom Drew, "yew hud Ow Bob, he'll give yew a tewne on his whissel, ont yew Bob?"

"I dornt know," say Ow Bob, "Thass tharsty wark."

In tha finish this feller agreed he'd give Ow Bob a try-out on his whissel, if so be we'd give a song.

"Now then," he say, "let's hare a rearl ow foke-song, like what yew sing of an evenin."

"We dornt sing a lot," say Fred Johnson: "dew we wor to sing tew loud, we'd hev Bumble tha policeman round to see what wor a-goin on."

"I'll look arter tha policeman," say this feller. So we struck up 'From Hare tew Etarnity'.

"Howd yew hard," hollered tha wireless feller, "thet on't dew."

"Thass poplar on tha wireless," say tha boy Chaarlie.

"Thet ent a foke-song," say this feller.

"He mean suffin old," say Tom Drew. So we staarted orf agin with 'Nellie Dean' and we went right tha way trew it without tearkin no notice o' tha wireless feller a-hollerin. Time we'd done, he say, "Thass tew well known."

"Yew dornt want much, dew yer?" I say.

Howsomever, Ow Bob fetched his tin-whissel an staarted to play a tewne what none on us dint know, ceptin we'd hud him play it hisself. 'Ploughin all day' thet wor called, an Ow Bob reckoned thet wor a good ow Dumpton song. Tha wireless feller mearde him sing it tew us till we knew tha wards.

* * *

Then a few nights arterwards, he come back with a lot o' machinery an some more fellers. They hed a bit of a job, so they reckoned cos we hant got tha electrick in Dumpton. Time they wor ready, tha wireless feller held a thing up tew his gob an say: "And now we wisit tha little willage o' Dumpton, where yew can still hare tha old songs sung like they wor in tha days o' our ansesters, gathered hare in thet anshent inn, tha Fox, arter a hard day's toil in tha filds. Lissen tew Mr Robert Blewitt, a hale ow man o' 89, as he mearke merry on his tin-whissel, leading tha woices o' his fellow-willagers in a familiar tewne..."

Then he wearved his hand for us to staart, an I prooged Ow Bob in tha ribs an orf he went. Mind yew, we wor a-singin this hare song in a different key from him for a bit, but I reckon thet fared to come out alright. So dew yew want to hare suffin warth harin, dew yew lissen to yar wireless sets when this hare programme come on.

HARBERT
7th May, 1954

TIME MA LAY ABED

I never did tell yer about our Boy Scouts an their bob-a-job. My Ma got took quare an hed to stay in bed. Har stummick is suffin gastrick. Well, bor, thare she lay abed with this hare gastrick stummick, an I hed to git my own meals an hars tew. I wor jest a-clarin away tha breakfast things when tha door knocked, an thare stood one o' them young 'uns from tha Fen Cottages. "Ha yew got a bob-a-job, mister?" he say.

41

Now them thare kids from tha Fen Cottages, they're a rum ow lot, they are. I wor right pleased to see one on em a-dewin suffin yewseful for a chearnge. "Come yew on in , bor Arther," I say. "I're got jest tha job for yew. Yew can dew this hare washin-up."

* * *

Well, arter I'd picked all tha bits o' my Ma's best china up orf tha floor, I hed harf a mind not to give tha young warmin tha bob arter all. Then I thowt to myself thet'd be a shearme not to give it tew him, cos thet ent for him but for tha Scouts, an thass suffin what want encouragin like in them kids, dewin suffin for other pearple. Besides, I felt sorry for him, standin thare without no uniform, cos his father is tew poor to buy him one. So I give it tew him, an orf he sailed.

Then my Ma hollered from upstares: "What wor thet row? Thet fared to sound like yew brook tha cups an sorcers."

"Thet wornt narthin, Ma," I say. "I dropped tha poker."

"Cos dew thet wor them cups an sorcers what yew brook, boy Harbert," hollered my Ma, "yew on't never hare tha larst on it." Then tha door knocked agin, an thare stood another o' them kids from tha Fen Cottages.

"Ha yew got a bob-a-job?" he say.

"Git yew out on it, boy Arnie," I say. "I jest give a bob-a-job to tha boy Arther."

"He ent in tha Scouts," say tha boy Arnie.

"What?" I say, "he come in hare brearkin all my Ma's best china an he ent in tha Scouts?"

"What did I hare yew say about tha china?" hollered my Ma from upstares.

"Narthin, Ma," I say, "I jest say tha pearpers reckon thass a rum ow job in Indo-China."

"Thass right," say tha boy Arnie, "tha boy Arther never hev bin in tha Scouts. Yew arst tha scoutmarster."

"I'll give it tew him when I ketch him," I say. So I took tha boy Arnie inter tha kitchen an I say tew him, I say, "Tearke yew this hare stickit an stick yew all these hare bits o' china back together agin. An tearke yew this hare bob, jest in case yew're done afore I git back, cos I'm a-goin arter tha boy Arther."

* * *

Corse, I knew whare he'd gone. Time I got to Mrs Higgins's shop he'd jest left. I ketched him up by tha blacksmith's an I say, "Yew ent a Boy Scout."

"I never sed I wuz," he say.

"Then give yew me thet thare bob back," I say. "I're spent it," he say.

"What did yew spend it on?" I arst. "Chocklet," he say.

"Then give yew me tha chocklet," I say. "I're et it," he say.

"Then I'll lay inter yew, yew young warmin," I say.

"Yew dussn't," he say, "dew I'll tell my father o' yew."

I ent chicken-harted in tha yewsual way, but his father is a big bull-necked feller what wor in tha nearvy durin tha war.

Time I got back hoom thare worn't no sign o' tha boy Arnie, an them bits o' china still lay thare. Thare worn't no sign o' my tewbe o' stickit neither, an harf tha apple dumplins wor gorn outer tha larder. Then tha door knocked agin, an fower or five Boy Scouts stood thare in their yewniforms. "Ha' yew got a bob-a-job, mister?" they say.

"I'll gi' yew bob-a-job," I say. "I're jest give tha boy Arnie a bob an dew I hev any more on it I'll give tha hull lot on yer a ding o' tha lug."

"He ent in tha Scouts," say one on em.

"What did yew say?" I say.

"He ent in tha Scouts," say this nipper.

"I're hed enough o' this hare," I say, "dew yew go orf hoom, tha lot on yer."

"Yar gearte want mendin," say another o' them boys.

"Oh no thet dorn't," I say.

"Oh yes thet dew," he say, "we see tha boy Arnie hull a brick at it."

My hart, if he worn't right. One o' tha crorss-bars wor brook right trew, an thare lay a duzzy greart brick. I got a bit o' wood an a saw an a hammer an nearls, an give them Scouts tha job o' mendin it. They done it alright, tew, so I give em five bob. Then I got tha gal Alice to come round an look arter my Ma time I sailed orf to Flitmarsh an got some new china afore she found out.

I reckon dew I wor to send a bill into them boys' fathers for tha mornin's wark thet'd corst em a week's wearges apiece.

HARBERT
28th May, 1954

SUFFIN IN THA WIND

I ent never known Humpty Potter to go in much for flowers. So I dint know what to mearke on it when he went orf to Bumble, our policeman, an lodged a complearnt about somebodda pinchin a lot o' plants outer his yard.

"Salvias," he say, "thass what they wor. I hed a few duzzen in boxes a-hardenin orf ready to set out in my front garden, an now they're gorn."

I ent a-sayin nartin what I carnt pruve, but when I hud about Humpty a-goin to Bumble I thowt to myself, thare's suffin in tha wind.

Bumble come in tha Fox thet night an he say, "Ha yew hud about them flowers bein took outer Potter's yard?"

"Ah," I say, "thass a rummun ent it?"

"Ah," he say, "thet it is. I'm jest a-goin down thare now to keep watch."

"Whass tha yewse o' thet?" I say, "now them flowers a gorn?"

"They ent all gorn," say Bumble, "thare's still a few left what tha feller coun't carry tha fust time. Potter reckon he might come back an git tha rest, an I'll nab him when he dew."

"Why carnt Humpty keep watch hisself?" arst Tom Drew.

"Cos he's gotta go out tonight to some meetin or another," say Bumble.

Tom give us all a look, but he never say narthin.

"What worry me," went on Bumble, "is my own garden. I're got a lot o' salvias myself. I're bin a-growin on em under glass an now they're out a-hardenin orf, an what a feller dew round Potter's he can dew round mine."

I looked at Tom Drew an he looked at me, an tha searme thing come inter our hids at tha searme time. "Whare's yar missis tonight?" we both arst.

"Thass tha trouble," say Bumble, "she's orf to tha wimmen's Institewte an nartin I could say would stop her."

"Then yew want to go hoom an stay thare," say Tom. "I're got my dewty to dew," say Bumble.

So orf he went to Humpty Potter's an got in tha shud an stayed thare a-garpin trew a knot-hole till all hours.

* * *

44

Nexter mornin I see Bumble comin down tha rood on his bike an he looked suffin riled. "Did yew ketch him?" I arst.

"No, thet I dint," say Bumble, "but thare ent a salvia left in my garden, not one. Thass right enough what Potter say, thare's some feller a-goin round a-pinchin pearple's flowers an I'll git him yit."

Well, that wor tha Wednsda, whass market day at Flitmarsh, so I took time orf and hed a hop over to Flitmarsh to see what I could see. My hart, if Humpty dint stand thare on tha market with a couple o' boxes o' salvias an a duzzen empty.

"Mornin, Humpty," I say, "sellin salvias?"

"No. bor,' he say, "I're bin a-buyin some."

"Git yew out on it," I say, "yew fare to a bin sellin em, by tha looks o' these empty boxes."

"Yew want to be careful what yew say, Harbert, bor," say Humpty, "thare's a law agin sayin things like thet thare about pearple."

"Then what about these hare boxes?" I say.

"These hare salvias wor tha larst what the feller had," say Humpty. "An when I bowt tha lot he trew in tha boxes for tha searme price. They'll come in handy to me."

"Dew yew mean to stand thare an tell me yew want all these hare salvias for yar garden?" I say.

"Now look yew hare, Harbert," say Humpty, "yew're bin a good friend to me an I're bin a good friend to yew. I dornt like to hare yew say things what might git yew wrong with me. Thet ent like yew."

"Yew're got enough thare for tew gardens," I say.

"Thass right," say Humpty, "thass jest what they're for – tew gardens, mine an Bumble's. Seein as how Bumble lorst all his salvias tryin to ketch tha feller what whipped mine, I thowt tha least I could dew wor to buy him some more. Yew ent got narthin agin thet, ha' yer?"

* * *

I stuck my bike on tha back o' Humpty's cart an come hoom with him. On tha way we stopped at Bumble's, an Humpty give him a box o' these hare salvias. "Thass for yar trouble," he say.

"Thass marster good on yer, say Bumble.

"Thet ent narthin," say Humpty.

Then Bumble garped at tha box. "My hart," he say, "git yar glimmers on thet – I marked all my boxes an thare's tha mark."

45

"Well, I'll be blowed!" say Humpty: "thet jest show, dornt it. That thare feller I bowt em orf in tha market must a bin tha one what took em from yars. Yew want to git over to Flitmarsh right quick, bor. He's a tall feller with ginger hair an a squint in one eye."

HARBERT
4th July, 1954

THASS THA WAY O' THA WARLD

I ent sayin narthin about tha Norfick Show cos yew all see it searme as what I done. Tha marster run us up in his lorry on tha second day, like he allers dew, an we're bin a-mardlin about it in tha Fox ever since. Ow Bob Blewitt never went – he's tew old now for thet thare – so we hed to give him tha up an down on it, an tha way tha pore ow feller shearke his ow hid yew'd wonder what tha warld wor a-comin tew.

He's right about one thing – yare arter yare they git more and more o' this hare mashinery for dewin things what we allers yewsed to dew by hand, till one o' these days thare on't be no farm learbourers left, only injineers. Still, thet a gotta come, hant it? I mean, thass tha way tha warld is a-goin, ent it? Yew carnt stop it, can yer?

* * *

Ow Bob Blewitt reckon tha warst day's wark what they ever done wor to give up yewsin hosses an bring in these hare trackters. Trackters dornt give no muck, he say, an them thare fartilisers ent tha searme thing, an one fine mornin tha farmers'll wearke up an find they ent got no goodness left in tha land.

What dew it matters, he say, dew one mashine can dew tha wark o' twenty men, when thet tearke twenty men to mearke tha mashine in tha fust plearce? Thass goin tha long way round to git nowhere, he say. Thass like goin to Norwich to ketch a bus back to Fumbleham, when yew could walk it in half an hour.

Besides, he say, tha grub dornt git no cheaper, thet keep gittin darer. Thass like he say in tha Fox only larst night, he say, "Thass all werra well yew hevin all this hare mashinery, but when I wor a young un we hed butter on tha tearble – now yew carnt afford it. Yew spend yar time milkin cows with milkin-mashines, an then yew go hoom an eat marj."

There's this thow, there ent many farm learbourers what want tew see that old days come back. Nor yit farmers, neither. They keep a-grumblin, but they ent sellin up cheap like what they done afore tha war. I say tew Ow Bob, I say, thass more mashinery they keep a-hollerin for, not less. My marster, now, he ent got but tew hosses left, Daisy an Prince, and when they're gorn he on't git no more.

*   *   *

Corse, thass all werra well seein all this new-fangled mashinery in tha Shows, but a lot on it ent no good to Dumpton. Me, I ent like Ow Bob, I're got my life ahid o' me, an I want to see Dumpton go with tha times. We're got some o' tha best land in Norfick hare an thet mean some o' tha best land in tha warld, but to see some o' our farms yew'd never think it.

We shan't dew much good till we git tha electrick an tha water laid on. Tha electrick come as far as Fumbleham an there thet stop. Tha marster, he're got one o' them dinymos in a shud, what run tha milker an give a bit o' light, but dew yew arst me thass more trouble 'n what thass warth.

He're got a bore for his water an a pump what go on petrol, but I shan't never forgit tha Chrissmass mornin thet went wrong. Tha fellers what come to mend it wornt proper exparts, cos there wornt none o' them warkin over Chrissmass, and they let suffin drop down that bore an block it. I tell yer, we dint dew narthin for days but run backards an forrards with buckets o' water from tha pump in tha yard o' one o' tha marster's cottages.

*   *   *

Us willagers, we still yewse lamps with parafeen oil an git our water outer wells what hant got none in when thass dry. Tha Beethoe an Bedstead Rewral Districk Cownsil a bin a-talkin for yares about layin that water on, but they dornt fare to dew narthin else but talk. I reckon tha money they spent sendin tha water-cart round in dry summers would a paid for layin that water on twice over.

Larst time somebodda imitearted to raise tha matter in tha Cownsil, tha feller what done all tha shoutin agin it wor him what dew tha contractin for tha warter-carts. Then thare's Ow Mother Quail from Dumpton Hall, har what repersent us, she dornt dew narthin. Thass alright for har, she're got a pump an when thet go wrong she git tha men in to fix it. But dew they wor to lay tha water on to Dumpton, thet'd corst har a penny or tew gittin tha pipes connected to tha housen, cos moost on em belong to har. I tell yer, thass a rum ow job. But dew yew arst me, thet carnt go on like this hare a lot longer.

HARBERT
9th July, 1954

THA LIFE O' BLISS

I reckon Bartholomew Smith must wonder how he come to marry tha skewlmistress. Ever since she got har claws intew him she're give him a rough ow time.

Now she're duzzy nare killed him, an if he ent layin in tha horspital a-figgerin out how much a diworce'd corst then my nearme ent Harbert.

I see him one mornin a-fribblin about in tha marster's tew-acre alongside tha Diddlin rood. Thet coun't a bin a lot arter six o'clock. I say tew him, I say: "For a man whass retired yew're up arly, ent yer?"

"Ah," he say, "an will be tomorrer."

"On't yar missis let yew sleep?" I say.

"Thass har belief," he say, "an rightly so, as tha errand what bring me hare is best done afore tha heat o' tha day."

"An what dew yew think yew're a-doin on in our fild?" I say.

"I'm a-seekin tha common agaricus," he say.

* * *

"Well, bor," I say, "yew on't find none o' them hare. Yew might find a few mushrooms if yew're lucky."

"Agaricus, my dare Harbert," he say, "is tha botanickal nearme for mushrooms."

"Then let them what talk botanickal stick tew it," I say. "Us hare in Dumpton talk English, an as far we're consarned they're mushrooms. An dorn't yew let tha marster see yew arter em, thass all."

I see him tree or fower days runnin, but I dint say no more. Then one day as I wor hoppin orf hoom for a bit o' dinner I see tha amberlance stood outside his house.

"Hent yew hud?" say my Ma, when I arst har who wor sick. "They reckon he's dead, or if he ent dead he ent far orf. Some say he took poison an some say he shot hisself. But I know diffrent – he hung hisself from tha beam in tha backus, thass what he done, he hung hisself."

* * *

Corse, thare wor thet many tearles went about thet wor a day or tew afore we got tha rights an wrongs on it. As nare as I know, what happened wor this hare.

His missis hed him out o' bed pickin mushrooms at harf arter five in tha mornin, an then she fried some with a bit o' bacon for their breakfusts. Then she went inter tha skewl, whass all joined on to tha house. She wor right in tha middle of a singin lesson when thare come a tappin at tha winder. Tha kids stopped on tha top note o' "Arly one mornin" an some on em shruck, an then she see har husband stood thare outside tha winder lookin like suffin come up for tha Larst Judgment.

She rushed out, but by tha time she got thare he'd fell down in tha playground an wor rollin about holdin his stummick.

"I'm sick," he say.

She got him inter tha house. Mrs Walpole, what charnced to be goin by, give har a hand, and from what she say tha ow gal dint think thare wor a lot wrong with him at tha time.

"Them men," she say to Mrs Walpole, "they git a bit of a pain an they think their number's up."

Howsomever, Mrs Walpole reckon she dint like tha look on him harself, an told tha ow gal she ought to hev tha doctor tew him.

"Nonsense," say tha skewlmistress. "he're bin like this afore. I'll lay thass on account of I told him to git tha fowl-house mended today."

* * *

What happened arter thet I dornt know, but she must a come round to Mrs Walpole's way o' thinkin, cos, as I say, tha amberlance come about dinner-time an took him orf to tha horspital.

Thass plain enough now what he done. He must a went an picked a totty little ow toodstewl along o' them mushrooms, an his fewl of a

49

missis must a went an cooked it. Corse, all tha wimmen reckon thass his fault for pickin it, but us men reckon diffrent. Like Fred Johnson say in tha Fox, thass a woman's job to watch what she cook. I mean to say, if a man bring hoom a cabbage orf tha allotment, his missis dornt go an cook it slugs an all, dew she?

* * *

Now tha rum thing about it is this hare. Time she wor a-hookin on him, Miss Fitch (what wuz) dyed har hair red, kept har tongue whare thet belong, an went about like she wor twetty-five stead o' fifty-five. My hart, if she hent gorn an dyed har hair agin!

Tha fust one to see it wor Mrs Higgins from tha shop, what wor goin by when tha ow gal wor a-gittin inter a taxi with a greart ow bunch o' flowers to tearke to tha horspital.

"I should hate to think of anythin happenin to my Barty," tha ow gal say to Mrs Higgins.

Dew yew arst me, he on't hev har mobbin on him mornin, newn an night when he git hoom. Not for a day or tew, anyhow.

HARBERT
15th July, 1955

SHILLIN DOWNSTAIRS

Tha gal Alice wanted to go to tha seaside last Saturday, but by the time we got to Flitmarsh thare wornt no more trearns for Cromer nor yit Wells. We could a got as far as Melton Constable an picked one up for Norwich, only tha feller reckoned thet'd git inter Norwich jest in time to miss all tha quick uns to tha sea. Like thet we might a got to tha sea in time to come hoom agin, an we would a done, jest for tha trip, only tha feller pearke in his book an told us we woun't git hoom agin afore tha Monda.

What with cyclin from Dumpton with tha gal Alice on tha step, I wor thet hot I hed to tearke my weskit orf. I left my bike at tha back o' tha Duck an Drearke, an we went inside for a drop o' suffin yo kewl orf with.

I say to tha landlord, I say: "Thass a thongy ow day, ent it?"

"Ah," he say, "tha wireless reckon thass eighty-fower degrees on tha Air Ministry roof."

"Whare's thet?" I say.

"On top o' tha Air Ministry, I reckon," he say.

"Is thet a big buildin?" I say.

"Oh ah," he say, "Thass as big if not bigger than tha cinema acrorst tha way."

"Yew'd think thare'd be a bit of a breeze up thare, woun't yer," I say, "what with all them aircraft comin in to land."

"Talkin o' tha cinema," say tha gal Alice, "I wonder whass on?"

"Thare's a good un on today, mor," I say. "Thass called 'China Seas', an thet's a got Clark Gable in it, an Jean Harlow."

"Ent she dead?" say tha gal Alice.

"She wornt when they took this film," I say.

* * *

So orf we sailed acrorst tha way to tha cinema, what used to be tha corn market at one time. I got a couple o' shillin tickets (I allers dew git good seats when I tearke tha gal Alice), an tha mawther at tha door say, "If yew tearke my adwice yew'll set upstairs."

"We allers set downstairs," I say. "Thet mearke tha gal Alice giddy settin up top."

"Thass yar own lookout," she say, "but I adwise yew to go up."

"Now look yew hare, mor," I say, "if I want to set downstairs I set downstairs, an if I want to go up I go up. Thet hent got narthin to dew with yew."

"Thass right, Harbert," say tha gal Alice, "dew yew stick up for yarself. Silly-bold mawther, she want tearkin down a peg or tew."

Well, we went inside an set down, an my hart if thare wornt a lot o' hollerin a-goin on. They staarted to play a tune, an all tha pearple cheered rheir hids orf. Then harfway trew tha tune they staarted a-booin, an they kept a-booin till tha cartains drew aside an writin come on tha screen. Then they cheered a duzzy site louder'n they done afore.

* * *

"They're a rowdy lot, ent they?" I say.

"There's a lot o' kids," say tha gal Alice.

I staarted to read what thet said on tha screen, but I dint hev time to mearke out no more'n harf a dozen letters afore suffin went down tha back o' my neck with a splosh. I let out a yell, an tha gal Alice got har handkerchiff tew it.

"What is it?" she say.

"I dornt know," I say, "but thass suffin cold."

"Thass ice cream," she say.

"I'll soon settle thet," I say, an I got a handful o' this hare ice cream orf o' my neck an hulled it back whare thet come from.

Yew should a hud tha hollerin upstairs! Thet thare ice cream fare to a brook up an hit tree or fower on em.

"Thet'll larn em," I say.

*   *   *

But I hent hardly got tha words out o' my mouth afore a bit o' orange skin knocked tha gal Alice's hat orf, an tha stopper out o' a lemonade bottle caught me a ding alongside tha skull. I got up an tarned round an hollered, an got my gob full o' monkey nuts.

"Set down and tearke no notice," say tha gal Alice, "thass only kids."

I wornt hevin thet. I sung out to tha mawther at tha door, but all she say wor, "If yew'd gorn upstairs like I told yer, tha kids upstairs coun't a slung things down atop on yer."

So we set quiet an watched tha film. Thet wor all about some feller called 'Space-ship Dan' what went orf to tha moon to reskew tha Princess o' Mars from tha clutches o' tha Marster-Mind o' tha Planets. He wor harf-way thare in this hare space-ship when a feller from Venus, what hed tew snouts an a tail like a duzzy squirrel, hulled a spanner inter tha jet ongine.

"I dornt think a lot o' this," say tha gal Alice.

"Nor yit dornt I," I say, "but we'll hatta stick it, cos I paid a shillin apiece for these hare seats."

*   *   *

Howsomever, jest as tha wolcano on tha moon staarted shootin out fire an tha space-ship fell right bang intew it, thet say, "See what happen next week," an come tew a stop.

"Thass good," I say, "Clark Gable come on next."

But Clark Gable never come on next. Thet wor Mickey Mouse, an arter him come Felix that Cat, an arter him come Tom Mix an his hoss, an then a greart big feller called Superman what flew about on a sort o' cape like what our policeman wear. Then come some more cowboys, an then come 'God Searve tha Queen'.

I told tha mawther I wanted my tew shillin back, but all she say wor: "Carnt yew read? Clark Gable ent till tonight. If yew want to come marchin inter tha children's matiney as bold as brass, thass yar lookout."

HARBERT
22nd July, 1955

SHOWTIME SPUFFLE

Tha Dumpton Amachewers hed a meetin tha other night. We done 'Jewlius Seizer' larst Chrissmas, but dornt yew arst me what we're a-goin to dew t'yare. Tha meetin brook up in a spuffle.

Ow Mrs Frorst staarted it orf. Arter tha Wicar, what wor in tha chare, hed said his bit about tha success o' larst yare's concert, she got up an hollered: "Afore we go any fudder, let me say hare and now we dornt none on us want no more o' thet thare Shearkspear. He're caused enough trouble in this hare willage already.

* * *

Corse, we all knew what she wor gittin at. They reckon thet wor larnin one o' them thare Shearkspear plays at skewl what mearde young Jimma Forster write a lot o' anomaious letters what duzzy nare split up Enoch Fletcher an his bride-to-be.

"My dare Mrs Frorst," say tha Wicar, "tha incident to which yew refar carnt dew narthin to rob Shearkspear of his reputearshun as the greartest poet this hare country hev perduced. I feel thet to choose a play by Shearkspear – if we choose wisely, for some of tha humour of our ancestors wor a bit broad for modern tearstes – would be to choose tha best England can offer. Howsomever, I hev an open mind."

"That thare Shearkspear wor a wicked man, an yew carnt tell me diffrent," say Mrs Frorst.

"Hare, hare," sung out some o' tha wimmen, and young Jimma Forster's mother shouted: "They never did ought to let them skewlmistresses stuff tha squit inter kids' hids – an yew can tell yar missis thet time yew get hoom Bartholomew Smith."

Smith, him what married tha skewlmistress, he up and say: "I resent thet remark. If parents looked arter their kids at hoom, they'd come to skewl to larn their lessons, not mearke mischief."

"Tha cheek on it," sharmed out Mrs Forster. "Nobodda ent a-goin to tell me I dornt bring up my kids proper! I shall want an apology out o' yew – in black an white."

* * *

Tha Wicar pearked round for suffin to hit that tearble with, an finally hit it with a ink-bottle. "Order! order!" he say. "We're gittin away from tha point. Tha question afore us is, what are we a-goin to parform t'yare?"

"I reckon we ought to dew a pantermime," say Fred Johnson.

"Are yew a-goin to be tha Dame?" arst tha boy Chaarlie.

"No, thet I ent," say Fred.

"Well, bor, someone'll hatta be," say tha boy Chaarlie.

"Thet ent right," say Mrs Frorst. "Dressin up in wimmen's clothes. I'm agin it, an so is tha Good Book. Thass tha searme as thet thare Shearkspear – thass wicked."

Ow Mother Quail got on har hind legs, wearved har ow shewtin-stick, an hollered: "Mr Chareman, a greart deal o' rubbish hev bin talked so far at this hare meetin, an unless yew exercise yar authority I foresee thet a greart deal more is comin. What few intelligent pearple thare are in Dumpton come to these meetins an carnt git a ward in edgeways.

"Now it is clare to me, espeshally arter larst yare's expearience thet to put Shearkspear afore a State-educated audience is to carst parls afore swine. Therefore, Shearkspear is out. Nor can we entertain so stewpid a suggestion as a pantermime. We hev no singers, no dancers, and no musicians. What we must dew is obwious. We must dew a quiet domestic play such as Wimmen's Institewtes parform throughout tha country. Now let us cease this idle chatter an choose one."

* * *

"Dew you know what I reckon we ought to dew?" arst Tom Drew, tha landlord o' tha Fox.

"I shall be glad of a suggestion," say tha Wicar.

"I reckon we dint ought to dew narthin," say Tom. "Thet ent narthin but a wearste o' time. Night arter night harf tha willage come hare to reharse. Thet interfare with tha proper soshal life o' tha pearple. They carnt dew this an they carnt dew thet cos tha Amachewers come fust. An whass it all for? Narthin."

Humpty Potter, he's quick, he see what wor in Tom's mind. "Thet keep em out o' tha pub, dornt it?" he say. "Thass whass worryin yew, Tom."

"I ent speakin as tha landlord o' Tha Fox," say Tom, imiteartin to look like he meant it, "I'm speakin as one of yew. Whare dew it get yer?"

My hart, if thet dint set Mrs Frorst orf agin.

"Now yew hare it, streart from tha hoss's mouth," she say. "Thet fare as if thare ent but tew things Dumpton pearple can dew with theirselves – go to tha Fox an drink theirselves silly, or come hare an dress up as wimmen an all sorts o' wickedness. Drew want yer to go darft his way, an thet thare Bartholomew Smith, what hent bin livin in tha willage above ten yare, want yer to mearke fewls o' yarselves with all this Shearkspear. I reckon thass time Dumpton pearple wook up an lived clean."

Corse, they dint let har git away with thet. An when I slipped out with Tom jest afore closin-time, some on em wor still argifyin.

HARBERT
30th September, 1955

HUMPTY'S DEWTY

I'll say this hare for tha Wicar, he may not know how to stand up to ow Mrs Frorst, but he dornt fear barglars. He come along o' us tha other night a-chearsin one what brook inter tha Hall, an come to think on it, thet might a bin better if he hent.

Whass more, thet might a bin better if he hent a said narthin at tha Mothers' Meetin about Dumpton and Diddlin bein run together inter one parish, cos then tha Rewral Dean woun't a bin comin to see him. But I'd best staart at tha beginnin.

Ow Mother Quail an har son a bin away from tha Hall for a bit, an tha butler see his charnce to go an wisit his sister (so he reckon), so thare wornt nobra thare tha other night but tha gal Ethel whass harf light. Them thare barglers fare to know whass a-goin on in pearple's houses, an this one nipped in right quick and tied tha gal Ethel up in tha pantry an mearde orf with tha silver.

He'd a got clean away if thet hent a bin for Humpty Potter what ent no fewl, and charnced to be out round tha Hall to mearke sure Ow Mother Quail hed a few less pheasants to come back tew. Humpty see this hare bargler come out o' tha scullery winder with a sack on his back, an he dint like tha look on it. I mean to say, goin arter pheasants in yar own willage is one thing, but when these hare furriners come hare laying their hands on other pearple's property, thass criminal.

* * *

Knowin his dewty, Humpty went arter this feller, but he jammed on a dead brarnch an tha feller hud it an run. So Humpty fired orf a charge o' shot at him an thet wook up MacBrain, tha gearmekepper. Afore long thare wor hart a dozen on em a-runnin arter tha bargler, an we all went up from tha Fox arter tha boy Chaarlie come tearin in to tell us thare wor suffin funny goin on. Time we got thare MacBrain had copped Humpty an they wor goin at it hammer an tongs, but jest then tha gal Ethel got tha dish-clorth out a har gob and shruck, and thet dint tearke long to mearke sartain Humpty wor speakin tha trewth.

Corse, tha bargler might a got away by this time if he'd a known whare he wor a-goin, but what with him bein a furriner an thet being dark as pitch he got hisself cornered in tha spinney back o' tha Wicaridge Loke. Thass how tha Wicar come to join in, cos he hud tha hollerin an thowt thet wor his plearce as parson to see thare wornt no wiolence among his flock. So he stuck on his ow hat, what look like a billycock someboddy a sat on, armed hisself with a ebony rod what he use for a rewler, an sailed up tha loke.

* * *

56

Now this hare bargler hed left his car on tha Diddlin rood, tha other side o' tha Hall, an he knew well enough he count git back tew it without us ketchin him. Thare wornt but one thing he could to dew – drop tha sack o' silver so as he could run quicker, an then hop acrorst my marster's ten-acre to tha Flitmarsh rood an charnce his luck. Well, thass what he done, an time we wor beatin trew tha spinney lookin for him he wor comin trew tha hedge on to tha Flitmarsh rood an arstin hisself whare he should go next.

This is whare tha Rewral Dean come in. Jest as tha bargler popped trew tha hedge, tha Rewral Dean, ow Canon Shott, wor comin up tha Flitmarsh rood in his little ow car on tha way to see tha Wicar.

Canon Shott hed a lot on his mind, part from tha fack thet his rare-light hed gorn out an he wor wondering if he'd run inter Bumble, our policeman. He needn't a worried about thet, cos Bumble wor settin at hoom fillin in fowerteen forms about one o' Enoch Fletcher's pigs what a staarted to sneeze.

But he hed plenty else to worry about, cos he're bin gittin inter hot water about tha way them rewmours are a-goin about consarnin our parish being marged with Diddlin Parva, an he wor setting thare grippin his steerin-wheel as if thet wor our Wicar's troot. "Once an for all," he wor sayin tew hisself, "I wish to mearke it clare thet as Wica o' Dumpton it is yar dewty..." when all of a sudden he hed to step on tha brearke right sharp cos a feller wor in front o' tha car a-wearvin his arms.

When tha car pulled orf agin, anybodda who dint know diffrent might a thowt tha Rewral Dean wor a-drivin on it. They woun't a noticed as how tha jacket woun't dew up an tha collar wor pinchin inter tha neck like a bit o' string round a leg o' ham. As for tha feller what stood on tha grarss varge, tha Rewral Dean's own dorg would a gorn for him an tore tha seat out o' his trousers. Pore ow Canon Shott hed come tew in his underwear, an bein suffin rafty for tha time o' yare thare wornt narthin he could dew but put on tha clothes tha bargler hed left lyin in a heap.

* * *

Arter thinkin hard for tew minnits, Canon Shott found hisself proper boilin. He hent bin so riled since tha day his hid choirboy let orf a squib in charch. "Hare," he say to hisself, "is suffin else tha Wicar o' Dumpton a got tew arnser for. If he carnt calm down tha rowdy element in his parish,

57

an mearke if searfe for his superior o' tha clorth to pay him a soshal wisit, then thass time he arst hisself whether he're found his wocation."

With thet he clenched his fists tighter than what parsons dew as a rewle, an staarted marchin orf to tha Wicaridge to tell tha Wicar a thing or tew. He hent gorn above harf-a-dozen steps afore he stopped. "My hart alive!" he say, or whatever thet is parsons dew say when they're flummoxed, "how can I appare before a jewnior member o' tha Ministry in this hare clobber? What will his wife think? What would tha Bishop say? I should be tha larfin-stock of tha die-or-cease! Oh, tell it not in Gath!"

But he dint hev time to think what else he could dew, cos we'd got tha scent by then, an we come runnin acrorst tha ten-acre like one o'clock. Tha Rewral Dean took one look at his baggy trousers, tightened tha wropper round his neck, give tha peak o' his cap a tug, an sailed orf down tha rood as farst as what his legs would carry him. An if yew want to know what happened arter thet, yew'll hatta wait till next week.

HARBERT
28th October, 1955

TEW AT THA STEARTION

Thet ent once in a lifetime a rewral dean find hisself hangin by tha breaces from a shandyleer. Howsomever, thass whare I left our Rewral Dean, ow Canon Shott, arter tellin yer larst week how he got mistook for a bargler.

Thet thare bargler what brook inter tha Hall mearde tha ow Canon chearnge clothes with him, an afore long thare wor a score on us a-chearsin on him. He run inter tha Wicaridge an hid hisself, an Hundredweight Hodge, our blacksmith, found him in tha clothes cupboard. So what did Hundredweight dew but hang him on tha shandyleer, an leave tha Wicar's missis a-guardin on him with a poker, time he went for tha policeman!

* * *

58

In tha meantime, things wor goin on tha other end o' tha willage. Bumble, our policeman, he dint know narthin about tha bargler cos he wor a-fillin in forms about one o' Enoch Fletcher's pigs. Arter he'd done, he wiped tha ink orf of his thumb an stuck his tewnick on, an feelin a bit dry he thowt thet wor time he went to see everathing wor being conducted proper down at tha Fox, He'd jest got his bike out when he see a car stopped down tha rood an a feller imiteartin to pump up one o' tha tires.

"Hello," say Bumble tew hisself, "whass a-goin on?"

When Bumble got close enough, he see this hare feller wore a parson.

"Whass yar tire flat, Reverend?" he say.

Tha parson took one peark at Bumble, jumped inter tha car, an pulled tha staarter.

"Hold yew hard a minnit, Reverend," say Bumble, "yew're left yar pump." He stewped down to pick tha pump up, an then he say: "Why," he say, "yew hent finished pumpin yit. There went no wind in this hare tire at all. Dew yew arst me, yew're got a punksher."

* * *

He would a said more, only tha car went orf like a duzzy rocket, leavin him stood thare with tha pump in his hand.

"Hey!" hollered Bumble. "Come yew back, yar rare light's out!"

Tha parson dint fare to want to come back, but tha ow car wor like a hoss – thet knew its marster wornt a-drivin it. Thet slewed round on tha barst tire an went hid-fust inter a gearte.

"Sarve yew right," say Bumble tew hisself, "for brearkin tha law!"

"Now then," say Bumble, gittin out his notebook an tarnin his flashlight on it. "I're got some questions to arst yew. With dew respeck to yar parson's collar, how dew yew come to be drivin without a rare-light, hinderin a officer in tha parformance o' his dewty, an drivin to tha dearnger o' tha publick, to say narthin o' dewin wilful dammidge tew a gearte?"

I'll lay Bumble hent never sin another parson dew what thet thare one done. Stead o' talkin tha matter over quiet, like what yew'd expect, he shot his fist out streart at Bumble's snout.

Now Bumble ent as slow as what he fare to look. Tha minnit thet feller lashed out at him, Bumble could tell he wornt up to no good. An thet come tew him like a streak o' lightnin as how he'd sin thet thare car afore, an thet belonged to Canon Shott. Whass more, this hare feller wornt Canot Shott. I tell yew, he's clever, Bumble is. An he ent no fewl when thet come tew a rough-house. In less time than thet tearke Dan Forster to put down a pint o' mild, Bumble hed thet feller sittin on tha hearth-rug in tha police-steartion hollerin for marcy.

"Now," say Bumble, "on top o' yar drivin offences we'll hatta add assaultin a police-officer an stealin a car. An I'll bet yew hent got no thard-party insurance neither. I dornt like seein a clargyman in yar position, but dewty's dewty."

Then he got on tha phone to tha hidquarters at Flitmarsh an told tha sarjint: "I're got a parson hare, an thass my belief he're gorn light. So yew'd best send a streart-jacket as well as tha Black Maria."

To git back to Hundredweight Hodge, he come sailin down tha rood an run bang intew us. We wor lookin up an down to see which way tha bargler went, an when Hundredweight told us he'd hung him on tha shandyleer in tha Wicaridge we dint wearste another minnit.

"Let's go an git him an tearke him to Bumble," say Fred Johnson. An orf we went.

We found tha Wicar's missis garpin at this hare bargler on tha shandyleer, with the poker in one hand an a pair o' steps in tha other.

"I wor jest a-goin to try to git him down," she say. "I believe thare hev been a terrible mistearke."

"Indeed thare hev," say tha bargler. "Release me at once from this uncomfortable an humilieartin position. Surely yew reckernise me as yar Rewral Dean, Canon Shott?"

"His fearce dew seem familiar," say tha boy Chaarlie.

"Whare's tha Wicar?" arst tha bargler. "He will identify me at once. Oh tha shearme o' hevin to request identifickearshun within one's own ruridecanal precincks!" (Thass a mouthful ent it?)

"I know it is he," moaned tha Wicar's missis, "leastways, I would if thet wornt for tha clothes."

"Tha Wicar stopped behind to look arter tha gal Ethel up at tha Hall," say Fred Johnson, "an thet ent for us to judge. He may be what he say he is an he may not. I reckon we ought to tearke him to Bumble."

"Dew what yew will," say that bargler, "but git me down, git me down!"

* * *

Well, together, we got him down an took him to Bumble.

"Thass Canon Shott, alright," say Bumble, "but what wor he dewin brearkin inter tha Wicaridge? Searvin yar Reverend's presence," he say, "but is thet part o' yar dewty as Rewral Dean to go around in thet thare clobber with house-brearkin impelliments in yar pocket?"

I never hud such a duzzy row in all my life as thare wor in Bumble's house for tha next ten minnits. An in tha middle on it Bumble got on tha phone an hollered: "I're got tew parsons hare now, an they're booth gorn light, so yew'd best hurry!"

HARBERT
5th November, 1955

DID YEW OR DINT YEW

Thare must a bin tha hull o' Dumpton in tha Flitmarsh police-court larst week when they hed thet thare bargler up for brearkin inter tha Hall. Harf on us wor witnesses, but tha other harf, moost on em wimmen, they tarned up to see pore ow Canon Shott in tha box.

Arter we'd took tha Canon to tha police-stearshun in mistearke for tha bargler, thet dint tearke long to see what hed rarely happened cos as yew know, P.C. Bumble already hed tha bargler thare dressed up in tha Canon's clothes.

My hart alive, thow, them cops dint harf arst a lot o' questions, an by tha time they'd done we dint know who'd done tha job – us, tha Canon or tha bargler. So when thet come to givin evidence, we hully did hev to watch what we wor a-sayin. An pore ow Canon Shott, him bein Rewral Dean an hevin a posishun to keep up, he hed to watch hisself more careful than tha rest on us put together.

* * *

This hare bargler, he fared to be a feller called O'Blamey, from London. Well, yew might a thowt thet would a done tha trick to staart with. I mean to say, any Bench in its right mind would a known a feller from London woun't be up to no good in Dumpton on a daark night, an would a sent him orf to jail without givin on him tha opshun.

But thet thare Flitmarsh Bench allers hev hed harf a tile missin. They let thet thare bargler an his lawyer say what they liked, an when he reckoned he hed a aunt in Norwich an another in King's Lynn, an lorst his way goin from one to tha other, nobra dint say narthin.

I tell yer, this hare O'Blamey hed one o' them clever lawyers down to look arter him. Feller called Hopp he wor, of a farm what sounded like Hopp, Skipp an Jump. Greart tall feller with a snout like a sparrer-hawk, all in black, with a ring on his finger like one o' my Ma's cartain-rings. We all stood up when he come in cos we thowt he must be tha Emperor o' China.

"Tell me," he say to Canon Shott, what stood in tha box a-chewin his lip an polishin his glarsses, "are yew subjeck to black-outs?"

"I...er...I dornt see tha relewance," say Canon Shott.

"Come, come, sir," say Hopp, "thass for tha Bench to rule whether a question cannot be put." (Thet thare Bench, whass asleep moost o' tha time, woun't never say narthin to noboddy.) "I must insist," went on Hopp, drorin hisself up like a skewlteacher talkin tew a kid pinchin apples, "thet yew arnser my questions when I arst em. Now, hev yew ever suffered from lorss o' memory?"

"Well ... er... I once," say tha Canon.

"Yew once..." say Hopp. "Only once? Think hard."

"If yew put it like thet," say tha Canon.

"I dew put it like thet," say Hopp. "Kindly stop prewaricatin an give me an arnser."

"Many yares ago, when I received a blow during a rugby match..." say Canon Shott.

"Tha time an tha plearce are no consarn o' tha Bench," say Hopp. "Yew admit, then, thet yew hev suffered from a black-out or black-outs in tha parst. Werra well. I will parss to my next point. Think carefully, sir. What wor yar fust reaction on findin yarself dressed up in tha somewhat staartlin attire in which yew wor found lurkin in tha wardrobe of a respectable Wicaridge?"

"I ... er... I wor amazed," say tha Canon.

* * *

"Exackly," say Hopp. "Yew wor amazed. Anyone who has hed a black-out an suddenly comes tew is bound to be amazed, dornt yew agree?"

"I must point out…," say tha Canon.

"Any pointin out to be done will be done by tha Bench," say Hopp, stickin his hands under his coat-tearls an bowin towards tha Bench what wor snorin fit to kill theirselves. "Now, sir, I arst yew, as one who has hed thet unhappy exparience, whether a man who suddenly wearkes up arter a lorss o' memory ent amazed."

"I spose he is," say tha Canon.

"An so dew I," say Hopp. "In fack, I know he is. An I fancy yew might a bin even more amazed if yew'd known what yew'd done time yew wor sufferin from thet thare black-out."

"Are yew suggestin …?" say Canon Shott.

"I ent suggestin narthin," say Hopp, "an kindly refrain from interruptin or I shall be forced to arst tha Bench to treart yew as a hostile witness. Now, are yew denyin thet durin yar black-out yew run yar motor-car inter my client, panicked, an for some reason probably unknown to yarself thet would tearke a skilled sickistrist to explearn, yew chearnged clothes with him as he lay unconshus by tha roadside, an run orf an hid in what to yar befuddled mind meant sanktewary – tha Wicaridge?"

"If I wor sufferin from a black-out, how could I a known if I did dew?" arst tha Canon.

"Percisely," say Hopp, bowin to tha Bench agin an smilin as if he'd jest won tha Sunda-skewl prize. "Yew mearke my point better than I could a mearde it myself. So yew dornt deny thet could a happened?"

"If, as yew say, I wor sufferin from a black-out, natcherally thet could a happened," say tha Canon, "except thet thet conflict with my carrickter an I ent admitted as I wor sufferin from no lorss o' memory."

* * *

Hopp's smile fell orf his fearce an he hollered: "Confine yarself to arnserin my questions, an kindly refrain from givin yar comments! Yew agree, as any rational man must, thet could a happened. Werra well. But let us examine tha consequences o' tha line o' thought yew began, quite improperly, to foller. Yew say yew hent admitted no black-out. Thare I must disagree, for yew quite plearnly, as tha record will show, mearde it clare thet yew suffered from a lapse of memory for at least some minnits, an possibly hours.

63

"But dew yew realise what yew are now puttin before tha Bench? In sayin yew hed no black-out, yew are arstin tha Bench to believe thet all thet unsavoury episode o' tha runnin down of a innocent pedestrian an tha chearnging o' tha clothes with a defenceless man wor carried out by a man – an a parson at thet – in full possession o' his faculties. I am mearkin tha kinder suggestion, based on tha history o' similar experiences yew hev suffered, thet all yew done yew done while yar memory hed temporily gorn. If yew prefar to say yew knew what yew wor dewin, I may hev to arst tha Bench for a adjarnment to hev yew medickly examined. Is thet a course which commend itself to yew?"

"I...er," say Canon Shott, what hent never bin so flummoxed since tha charch boiler barst durin tha confarmearshun.

But jest then tha chairman o' tha Bench, ow Colonel Nutt, wook up feelin marster hungry an adjarned for lunch. So I'd best adjarn an all till next week.

HARBERT
11th November, 1955

HARF A JAR O' JAM

I ent a-goin to tell yew no more about thet thare court kearse agin thet thare bargler what brook inter tha Hall. Yew're hud enough about tha barglery, an how ow Canon Shott got mixed up in it, to larst yew till tha kearse come afore tha Quarter Sessions. Cos thass whare thass a-comin up, an as far as what I can see pore ow Canon Shott is a-goin to hev a rum ow time on it in tha witness-box when thet dew.

I might a writ about how thet thare laywer Hopp done his best to git Canon Shott to say he done tha barglery hisself, an how tha chairman o' tha Bench snored thet loud durin tha evidence they hed to git tha Clark to wearke him up, an how tha mawther what sarve dinners in tha Duck an Drearke reckon tha Canon wor as white as a duzzy sheet till he'd hed a "little suffin" on the quiet to buck him up. But thare a bin thet many things happenin in Dumpton time I're bin tellin yer this hare yarn I'll hatta let it be till we see how they git on at tha Quarter Sessions.

* * *

For a staart, I're hed another proper ow row with tha gal Alice. Well, thet wornt my fault. Thet wor all on account o' har sendin me a jar o' jam.

I hent sin narthin much on har since thet time we hed a bust-up over har goin darncin. Thass like Ow Bob Blewitt allers say, yew're gotta let em kewl orf. Then one day when I come hoom from wark I see this hare jar o' jam on tha tearble, an my Ma say to me, "Tha gal Alice sent yew this hare, tha hussy," she say.

I dornt go a lot on jam as a rewle, but this I will say, tha gal Alice know what she's a-dewin on. Thet thare jam wor marster tearsty. I ett harf on it at one go, an then I stuck my wropper on an drawed orf round to tha gal Alice's to thank har for it.

An charnce would hev it, she wornt in. Har father opened tha door, see me, an shut it agin. I pearked trew tha winder, an see him an his missis goin at it hammer an tongs. In tha finish tha gal Alice's Ma come an opened tha door harself, an say, "So long as yew hent got yar dorg with yar, yew can come in."

* * *

I allers did like goin to tha gal Alice's, cos thass one plearce I'm sure of a welcome. Howsomever, them tew stood thare like duzzy mawkins, without so much as a "Good evenin".

"Rum ow weather, ent it," I say.

"Huh," say tha gal Alice's Ma, an staarted polishin tha oven door with a ow sock.

"I come to thank tha gal Alice for thet thare jar o' jam," I say.

"Oh did yer?" say har Ma.

"Yew did, did yer?" say har father.

"Ah," I say.

"Why?" say har father.

Well, together, I carnt say as how I'd stopped to arst myself thet. I mean to say, when somebodda arst yew a question like thet thare yew dornt know what to say, dew yer?

"Thass rare nice jam, ent it?" I say.

"Thass tew good for tha likes o' yew," say har Ma, tarnin tha sock inside-out an staartin on tha tearble legs.

"He want another jar, thass what thet is," say har father.

"I wount be surprised," say har Ma. "He never done narthin yit without thare wornt suffin behind it."

"I told tha gal Alice, dint I?" say har father.

"Ah, thet yew did," say har Ma.

"Told har what?" I say.

"Tha trewth, yew good-fer-narthin, yew," say har father. "Yew an yar duzzy dorg are alike. Tha minnit my gal Alice got down thet thare jar o' jam to send yew, I told har, I say, 'Yew'd best not send it,' I say, 'cos he ent warth it. But if yew must send it, thet'll larn yew what he is. He'll dew one o' tew things,' I say; 'either he'll come round hare like a rocket, all smarmy, an all thet'll signify is he want another jar for narthin; or else he on't come nowhare nare tha plearce, an thet'll mean he dornt appreshiate a thing yew dew for him an hent got tha manners to say thankyer. So one way or another,' I say, 'he'll give hisself away'."

"An so he hev," say har Ma, givin tha larst tearble leg a clout fit to bust it.

"Ah, thet he hev," say har father. "An now yew can git out an stay out."

* * *

On my way hoom I run inter tha gal Alice. Leastways, she run inter me. When I see har comin I wor in thet much of a flummox I imitearted to slip trew tha hedge, but she ketched hold o' my jacket an back I come.

"Thas tha wrong time o' yare for buds-nestin," she say.

Well, I dint like to let on I'd jest bin round to hars dew she might a thowt I wor only arter another jar o' har jam, like har father reckoned. Then agin, I dint like to say narthin, dew she might a thowt tha opposite. I hed to dew a bit o' quick thinkin, an time I wor a-dewin it she say: "I're jest bin havin a JAM round."

"Oh," I say.

"Ah," she say, "an I're hurt my foot."

"How?" I say.

"Somebodda JAMMED on it," she say.

"Oh," I say.

"Ah," she say, "an thet dint harf give me a JAR."

I ent sayin tha gal Alice wor a-hintin at suffin, but then agin thare wor suffin in har tone o' woice what mearde me breark out all of a malt. I coun't think o' narthin but to run, an thass what I done, all tha way to tha Fox. An when I see har in tha shop tha nexter mornin she told me a thing or tew. An thare's a harf a jar o' jam left what I hent he'd tha appetite to touch.

HARBERT
25th November, 1955

THA SHOW O' SHOWS

Me, I reckon our concert t'yare wor better'n larst. Thet wor a proper concert, not thet thare Shearkspear like we done larst Chrissmas, what wor more trouble than thet wor warth.

We hed a bit o' singin, an a bit o' recitin, an some o' tha skewlgals done a darnce, an tha Wicar's missis played tha pianner, an one way an another all tha pearple reckoned thet wor tha best thing they're sin in Dumpton this many yare parst.

Bein as I believe in searvin tha best bits till larst, I on't say narthin yit aout me singin 'On't yew come hoom, Bill Bailey' with my own accompanying on tha spoons. Not as I'm saying thet wor tha best thing in tha concert, thow some pearple did arst me arterwards if I're a-thinkin o' tarnin perfessional.

I'd best staart with Bumble, our policeman, cos he wor on fust. Leastways, he would a bin, only he stopped on tha way to run in Walpole tha farmer for not hevin no orfside light on his car. Thet mearde him a bit learte, an tha Wicar, what wor dewin tha announcin, called his nearme out tree times without narthin happenin. So Fred Johnson, what wor lookin arter tha lights (yew hatta watch them lamps cos tha drafts hully dew mearke them smoke), he hollered out: "Bumble ent hare yit, we'll hatta dew suffin else."

"I regret to say," announced tha Wicar, "as how our esteemed and talented parformer, Police Constable Edwin G. Bumble, a man as gifted in tha realms o' song as what he is in tha realms o' tha law, is unavoidably detearned for a few minnits."

"He never is thare when he's wanted," sung out tha boy Chaarlie, an tha pearple all larfed. They thowt thet wor part o' tha concert.

"He's chearsin Humpty Potter, I reckon," say Enoch Fletcher: "thass a fine night."

"Oh no he ent," sharmed out Humpty, stickin his skull trew tha cartains: "I're bin round tha back hare this larst harf hour, an I'm a-goin to do my conjurin tricks in a minnit."

"Whose rabbits are yew a-goin to pull out o' tha hat?" sung out tha boy Chaarlie.

"He's a-goin to pull a pheasant out of a bag," say Enoch.

Larf? Thet coun't a bin better if we'd a reharsed it.

"Order, please," say tha Wicar. "Thank yew. So while we weart for our esteemed and talented friend, Police Constable Bumble, I hev pleasure in arstin my wife to play a piece on tha pianner."

* * *

Well, his missis played 'Tha Bluebells o' Scotland', an seein as how Bumble wornt thare by tha time she'd finished, she played it agin. Then Bumble come in as she wor harf-way trew it for tha thard time, an he stood thare like a duzzy mawkin till she'd done , with all tha pearple a-clappin an a-cheerin an a-singin out "Good old Bumble!"

He got trew 'A policeman's lot is not a happy one' without no trouble, ceptin that tha pianner wor fower notes tew high for him, an Walpole set at tha back a-hollerin, "I'll gi' yew happy lot when I see yew in court!"

Then tha skewlgals done their darnce, what Mrs Frorst woun't look at cos she dint think thet wor proper, an Humpty tied tha Wicar up by tha neck an got Hundred-weight Hodge, our blacksmith, to pull tha rope. Yew should a hud tha pearple garsp, cos they dint know thet wor only a trick, an they all thowt thare woun't be no-one to give tha sarmon in tha charch tha nexter mornin.

Howsomever, I dornt know how he done it, but tha rope come away jest as thow we hent sin Humpty tyin knots in it a minnit afore an tha Wicar stood thare a-larfin. Mind yew, he dint larf so much when Humpty went an brook a egg inter his hat, an then dint know how to git rid on it.

* * *

Even ow Mother Quail done a item. She recited 'Come inter tha garen, Maud' by a feller called Alfred Lord Tennis-ball or suffin. An then, o' course, I done my song with tha spoons. Thet ent for me to say, but I ent no fewl when thet come to rattlin them spoons. Accordin to Enoch Fletcher, I could pick up a livin on Norwich Market any day. I shan't think o' dewin thet, thow, cos I hev enough trouble gittin my Ma to give me tha lend o' har spoons as it is.

We all say tha best bit wor when somebodda let on as Ow Bob Blewitt hed got his tin whistle in his pocket. Ow Bob, he wornt down on tha programme, but we mearde him git up on tha stearge an give us a tewne. He dint like it at fust, but arter he'd give us 'Rewle Britannia' an 'Tha British Grennerdeers' an harf-a-duzzen more, we hed a marster hard job gittin him orf agin. I thowt him tha best, an I told him so, but all he say wor: "What I carnt mearke out is this hare. Why dint thet thare mawther Maud come inter tha garden when tha feller arst har tew?"

HARBERT
16th December, 1955

MEETIN THA MEMBER

Our M.P. may be a Tory, but he allers hev a drink in tha Fox arter he're give a speech in Dumpton. He see tew it his meetins finish harf-an-hour afore closin time. Corse, we allers give him a bit of a rozzin.

He wor round hare tha other night. I reckon tha best part o' thutty pearple tarned up to hare him in tha Willage Hall, not countin them what went to boo. Another thutty wor weartin for him in tha Fox time he come down.

* * *

Humpty Potter stuck his hid in tha door an hollered, "Hare he come," so we all drunk up. Now he hent got no eleckshun expenses to worry about thet dornt matters if he stick his hand in his pocket. We dornt miss narthin in Dumpton.

"Stand back an let tha dorg see tha rabbit," say Ow Bob Blewitt, what set next tha fire.

'We're met afore, hent we?" say the M.P. when he see Bob.

"Thass right, marster," say Ow Bob, touchin his forrid with one hand an rattlin his mug with tha other. Tha ow hippercrit him, he never woted Tory in his life.

Howsomever, Ow Bob hed his mug filled for him, an so did tha rest on us, an then tha M.P. staarted talkin about tha crops. They ent fewls, them M.P.s, they know if they can git us talkin about farmin thet'll stop us talkin about ow Thorneycroft.

Thass whare Billy More-or-Less Hooper hed him.

"Thass a rummun," say Billy, "when yew're gotta go to tha Minister o' Agriculture to git tha country's finances sorted out ent it?"

"A werra good man, Mr Heathcoat Ainory," say tha M.P.

"I hent got narthin agin him personal," say Sam Cutch. "He give a good speech at tha Norfolk stockmen's dinner. I wor thare, so I know."

"Yew're a proper ow Tory, Sam," say tha boy Chaarlie.

"Thare ent no harm in bein a Tory," say tha M.P.

"Yew look well on it," say Ow Bob Blewitt, wearvin his mug about cos thet wor empty agin already.

* * *

"What I wor more or less gittin at," say Billy More-or-Less Hooper, "wor this hare. Look at all them what a bin more or less Charnseller o' tha Exchecker. Yew're hed Butler, hent yer, in a manner o' speakin, an then Macmillan an then Thorneycroft, stop me if I'm wrong, an now yew're more or less put in tha Minister o' Agriculture. An what a any on em done, so to speak? Narthin. More or less narthin."

"Under tha Soshalists..." say tha M.P.

"An another thing," say Billy. "If I may make so bold, what about what I might call tha Bank rate? Are yew a-goin to more or less stand thare an tell me thet hent got narthin to dew with Thorneycroft resignin? Are yer? Go on, are yer?"

"Thass right, Billy," say tha boy Chaarlie, "dew yew tell him."

"Tell him about tha stoon-pits, Billy," say ow Mrs. Wicks.

"Yew howd yar duller, mor," say Billy, "we dornt see yew in hare from one yare's end to tha next."

"Tha resignearshun o' Mr Thorneycroft," say tha M.P., "hent got narthin mystarious about it at all. I would arst yew to shut yar ears to rumour…"

"Winston Charchill," chipped in Ow Bob Blewitt, "Winston Charchill wor tha finest Hoom Secketary this country ever hed."

"We ent talkin about Winston Charchill," say Fred Johnson.

"Yew ent talkin about Winston Charchill," say Ow Bob, "but I am."

"Thass enough out o' yew, Bob," say George Bull, what think hisself clever. "Tha M.P. dornt want to hare what yew think."

"Whose beer am I drinkin?" arst Ow Bob. "Tom Drew, yew poured thet out. Who give yew tha money?"

Tom smiled an nodded at tha M.P.

"Alright then," say Ow Bob. 'If a gentleman buy me a pint, I'm entitled to parss tha time o' day with him, ent I? Who's a-goin to stop me?"

Nobra dint say narthin.

"Alright then," say Ow Bob. "This hare's betwixt me an him, an I say agin, Winston Charchill wor tha best Hoom Secketary this country ever hed. Thare ent one on yer can call me a liar."

"How dew yew mearke thet out, Bob?" arst Fred Johnson.

"Thass all I're gotta say, an I ent a-goin to say no more," say Ow Bob. "I wornt talkin to yew, I wor talkin to this hare gentleman what wor good enough to fill this hare mug, an look as if he might be thinkin o' dewin tha job agin."

Tha M.P. larfed an give a sign to Tom Drew.

"As I wor sayin about Mr Thorneycroft…" he say

"Afore yew go any fudder," say Billy More-or-Less Hooper, "let me more or less arst one question. Why did tha Cabinet kick Thorneycroft out when he wor dewin so well?"

"Dewin so well!" hollered Chaarlie. "Whose side are yew on?"

"I'm more or less a public man," say Billy, "an I more or less keep politicks out o' my public life. I, as it were, repersent this hare willage on tha Districk Cownsil, an I should be more or less sorry to see politicks interfere with local government. What I more or less say…"

He went on an on an tha M.P. never got another ward in afore closin time.

HARBERT

24th January, 1958

THA END O' OW BOB

Ow Bob parst away quiet in his sleep larst Friday night, or thet may a bin Saturda mornin. When his grandorter went in to scrub out, thare he lay in his bed in tha downstairs rume, jest like he wor sleepin.

I dornt know for sartain how old he wor, all I can say is he wor over nineta. Arter he got right old he used to add a couple o' yare on evera barthday, cos if he wor eighta-six he used to say, "I'm in my eighta-seventh yare," and then he used to start thinkin he wor eighta-seven, an next time he'd mearke out he wor eight-eight goin on eight-nine.

He're bin sort o' wandering in his mind for some time. We're only sin him in tha Fox on an orf, and then he hent hed a lot to say for hisself. Now an agin he'd staart talkin as if his own partner Hezekiah wor still alive.

* * *

The Wicar reckon he see him larst week go an stick a few primroses in tha jam-jar on ow Hezekiah's grearve. He just stood thare lookin at it, leanin on his ow stick, when tha Wicar come up an say, "Good arternune, Mr Blewitt." Accordin to what tha Wicar say, Ow Bob dint reckernise him. He arst tha Wicar for a light for his pipe – what show he wornt clare in his mind, cos he woun't never a smooked in tha charchyard ordinary – an then he say to tha Wicar, he say, "Thass a rafty ow day, ent thet, ow partner."

Corse, tha Wicar never hed no light on him, an he apolergised, an Ow Bob arst him, he say, "Dew yew wark on tha railway?"

When tha Wicar say no, he dint wark on tha railway, Ow Bob say, "Me an my ow partner Hezekiah, we warked on tha railway, but we dint like thet, we come hoom."

Then he say to tha Wicar, he say, "All this hare ground whare pearple lie," he say, "my ow partner Hezekiah allers dew say thass one bit o' ground they carn't tearke away. They can kick a man out o' his house an land, but this hare's one bit o' ground they carnt tearke away."

But afore he went off agin he fare to a reckernised tha Wicar cos he say "Reverend," he say, "dew yew read me what thet say on tha tombstoon." An when tha Wicar read it tew him he say, "No, thet ent tha one." Thet wor his fust wife's grearve what he wanted to see. He buried tew wives, did Ow Bob.

* * *

Then another time some o' tha kids see him alongside tha Pike Drain, standin right still, garpin at tha water. They got a bit scared on him, yew know what kids are like. One on em run up tew him an hollered, "Ow Bob Blewitt!" an then run away agin.

"Go on yew crow-keepers!" sung out Ow Bob. "Git yew yar wark done!"

They watched him an see him tearke his pipe out o' his mouth an peark at it. Then he drew on it a couple o' times an pearked at it agin, an then he hulled it in tha warter.

Tha nexter morning, so his grandorter reckon, when she went in to see tew him, he say to har, "I carnt find my pipe."

"Never yer mind, grandad," she say. "I'll bring yew a new un."

"I dornt want a new un," he say. "I sharn't be hare long enough to want a new un."

"Nonsense, grandad," she say.

But he wor right.

Thet might a bin tha searme day he say to har, he say, "Them ow larks are singin fit to bust."

"Go yew on, grandad," she say, "thass tew cold for larks."

He woun't hev thet.

"I hud tha barley-bud larst night, he say. "I wook up in tha night an thet wor settin on tha apple tree singin loud."

"Yer wor dreamin, grandad," she say. "Tha barley-bud, what yew call it, if thass tha searme as tha nightingearle, thet dornt come for a long time yit."

"I wook up an thet wor singin," say Ow Bob.

He hed a haard life, like moost o' them old uns. He never went away from Dumpton, ceptin to wark on tha railway for a bit when thet wor bein built, an I hev hud him say he took sheep to Ipswich once as a young man. Thare wornt narthin he wor more proud of than tha fack thet his greart-granfather's inishials are carved on tha bell-beam in tha charch steeple, his greart-granfather being one what helped to hang tha bell gittin on for 170 yare ago.

He never would hev narthin done for him. Many a time his grandorter a begged him to go an live with har, but thet'd a brook his hart to leave his cottidge, one up an one down. Tha Cownsil duzzy nare hed him out on it inter a hoom at one time, but we stopped thet. Thass only this larst yare or less his grandorter a got him to sleep downstairs. He used to reckon if he coun't sleep upstairs like a Christian he might as well be dead.

* * *

We hed tha fewneral on Wensda, an if I wor to tell yew who wor thare I'd hatta go trew evera nearme in tha willage. Tha chief mourners wor Mrs. Eliza Rudd (married dorter from Fumbleham) and Mr Rudd. Mrs Caroline Blewitt (widder o' tha learte Mr Dick Blewitt, his son), his grandorter an har husband an their children, an then one way an another a lot o' pearple in tha willage wor relearted tew him, like tha Forsters, his mother bein a Forster. Smith tha builder done tha undertearkin (his grandorter reckon they did think o' Chaarlie Merry at Flitmarsh, but they wanted to keep it in tha willage). Fred Johnson what wark for Smith, he mearde tha coffin outer a nice bit o' ellum with brass handles. An yew should a sin tha floral tribunes from far an nare. We sent one from tha Fox, an Tom Drew got thet mearde speshal in Flitmarsh in tha shearpe of a chair, cos Ow Bob a hed his own chair in tha Fox for more yares than what I can remember. Tha Wicar give a good address, an Fred Johnson give ow Dan a hand ringin tha bell.

Ow Dan he would ring tha bell hisself, he insisted on it. I ent sartain if he's the oldest inhabitant now. He's several tare younger than Ow Bob, an some say Billy More-or-Less Hooper's mother is older than him.

HARBERT
21st March, 1958

WICAR'S WHIST

Thare a bin a lot happenin in Dumpton this week. Ow Mother Quail fell orf har hoss an hart har knee, Mrs Higgins run har tricycle inter one o' Walpole's cows (thet dint hart tha ow cow), an tha Wicar hed another whist drive in that Willage Hall for his organ fund.

Bumble. our policeman, he got a bit funny about thet there whist drive. He see tha Wicar stickin a bill up outside tha Willage Hall, an he got orf o' his bike an he say, "Beggin yar paardon, Reverend," he say, "but I shall hatta arst yew to tearke thet down."

"Tearke thet down?" say the Wicar "Why?"

"No offence intended," say Bumble, "but that ent legal."

"Tha whist drive or tha bill?" arst tha Wicar.

Bumble took his helmet orf an scratched his hid. "Yew may well arst, Wicar," he say.

"I dew arst," say the Wicar.

"In thet case," say Bumble, "yew're entitled tew an arnser an if yew wor to arst me why I say thet ent legal, I should be obliged to tell yer. Yew'd be within yar rights, that I carnt deny."

"Percisely," say tha Wicar. "An I'm not only arstin yew why yew say thet ent legal, but what yew say ent legal – tha whist drive or tha bill?"

Bumble rubbed his helmet on his sleeve, put thet back on his hid, corfed, leaned his bike up agin tha palins, an say, "Without I wor to tearke a peark at tha right seckshun o' tha Act, I dorn't know as I could explearn it tew yer, not out o' my hid. But yew can tearke thet from me, thass an offence under tha Act."

"What Act?" arst the Wicar.

"Tha Act what cover whist drives," say Bumble. "Thass all laid down."

"Are yew tellin me whist ent legal?" arst tha Wicar.

"I ent sayin thet is an I ent sayin thet ent," say Bumble. "All I'm sayin is, thet thare bill a gotta come down."

"But my good man," say tha Wicar, "I carnt remember tha time when thare wornt a monthly whist drive in tha willage. An this one is for tha organ fund."

"Werra necessary, tew," say Bumble. "Thet thare organ want a bit o mendin."

"Well?" say tha Wicar.

Bumble look booth ways up tha rood.

"Thass like this hare," he say. "Betwixt yew an' me, I dorn't understand tha ins an outs on it myself. As far as what I'm consarned, yew can hev a whist drive evera night an twice on Sundas. But we're got a new sargent at Flitmarsh, he he're got some rum ideas. He fare to think yew're gotta hev police permission afore yew can run a whist drive, or thet may be a beetle drive, or thet may be booth – anyhow, thass suffin new to me – so if I dorn't know narthin about it, I carnt dew narthin, but if I see a bill sayin yew're runnin a whist drive I're gotta report it an tearke what ackshun tha sargent tell me tew. Leastways, thass what tha sergent reckon if I hent got thet wrong."

"Are yew suggestin," say tha Wicar, "thet I'm perposin to organise gamblin?"

"I dint say gamblin, Reverend," say Bumble. "I dint say one thing nor yit tha other. All I did say wor this hare, thet if yew dorn't stick up no bill I shan't know narthin about it, an if I dorn't know narthin about it thet dorn't matters what yew dew."

In tha finish tha Wicar took tha bill down agin, but he reckon he's a-gorn to look intew it. Corse, they hed tha whist drive on the Wensda but I wornt thare cos I dornt know narthin abowt caards. The gal Alice went, ah, my hart if she dint come hoom with a jam dish.

Thass tha fust time she're ever won anything at one o them whist drives, but she wor lucky cos she got Humpty Potter as har partner. Them wimmen fight like a lot o' ow cats to git Humpty for their partner, cos he allers win fust prize. I ent saying he cheat, but he allers fare to hev more kings an queens than what thare is in tha pack.

The gal Alice got herself inter a bit of a frap over thet there jam dish. Thet wornt har prize by rights, she won some fish knives an forks. They wor warth more'n thet thare jam dish, but ow Fanny Frorst wanted har to swap, so she acted sorft an swapped. Me, I woun't a swapped with ow Fanny Frorst if thet'd a bin for a sack o' soverins.

Howsomever, she wornt tha only one, cos thet tarned out tha boy Willie's missis won that there jam dish in tha fust plearce, an swapped thet with ow Fanny Frorst for a candlestick. Then when she got hoom tha boy Willie kicked up a row cos he reckoned he dint want no more candlesticks in his house, cos they woun't be no good to nobodda arter tha electrick hed bin laid on, and he dint like tha look o' this hare candlestick anyhow.

"Dew yew go streart back to ow Fanny Frorst an git yer jam dish back orf her," he say.

Well, his missis did say thet wor har prize not his, an thet wor a nice little ow candlestick, but in the finish she give in.

Corse, ow Fanny Frorst hung on to them fish knives and forks an told the boy Willie's missis if she wanted har jam dish back she'd hatta see the gal Alice.

She come round to ours werra nare in tears. "Well, thare," say the gal Alice. "I dorn't want no candlestick so I ent a'goin to give up this hare jam dish without I git tha knives an forks back."

As far as what I know, tha boy Willie's missis run orf back to ow Fanny and begged har to give the gal Alice them knives an forks back for the jam dish, and then let har hev the jam dish for the candlestick. Then ow Fanny come up hare an accused me o' putting har up tew it, an tha gal Alice sailed into ow Fanny an told har a few things about har family. Then my Ma got to hare about it an went for ow Fanny at the Wimmen's Institewte meetin, an Ow Mother Quail from the Hall, whass the prezzident, she hed to sort em out with har shewtin stick. Thet ent finished yit.

One way an another, thet thare whist drive wor a rum ow job. Tha Wicar's still imiteartin to find out what Bumble meant, an I reckon Bumble must wish he knew what the sargent meant.

HARBERT
18th April, 1958

THE HAARD OW DAYS

Thet want a bit o' thinkin about, dorn't it, tha way time fly? Hare's 1960 on top on us, but thare wornt narthin in Tom Drew's bottles at tha Fox larst night what could mearke us think o' anything good to say about tha 1950s.

"Thare's one thing," say Ow Dan Forster "thare's plenty o' money about, thow us owd-earge penshuners dorn't see a lot on it. I wor born in tha 1870's, an I sharn't see tha 1970s, an I ent sartain I want tew. But yew young uns dorn't know what hardship is. Yew dornt want for narthin."

"They never hed tha taxes to pay in yar young days, bor," say Fred Johnson "an things dint corst so much."

77

"Yew may talk," say Ow Dan. "Rorsin about on yar motor-bikes. I'll lay yew hed enough to eat on Chrissmas Day, an yar kids hed bewts on their feet an toys to play with."

* * *

He drunk up tha boy Charlie's pint my mistearke; an then arst me if I'd got any bacca cos he'd left his pouch at hoom.

"Ah," he say arter he'd stuffed enough o' my shag in his pipe to a larsted me a week, "I remember some hard ow winters. Thare wor one time if we hent a hed a sorft-harted cobbler I dorn't know what pearple'd a done."

"Arnie Carpenter?" arst Tom Drew.

"Thass him," say Ow Dan, "an a better feller I never did know, thow his missis wor a terrer. I remember tha frorst settin in shaarp right arter harvest, an thare wornt much wark about. Tha wearges dint come regler in them days. When thare wornt tha wark thare wornt tha wearges.

"Dick Moppett wor one o' them what wor haard hit. Dew yew could a pearked trew his winder, yew'd a sin his missis go to tha cupboard, git out tha jam-jar, count tha coppers in it, an set down with har hid in har hands. Dick come hoom one night arter traipsin all round lookin for wark, an his missis say, 'Dick, what are we goin to dew?'

"Thare wornt many men in tha willage what dint git arst tha searme question, an none on em coun't find an arnser.

" 'Dick,' say his missis', 'our little mawther want bewts.'

"'She want a doll for Chrissmas,' say Dick

"'She want bewts,' say his missis, 'she carnt git no fudder n' tha backus door without she git em.'

" 'She'll breark har hart if she dorn't git har doll,' say Dick

" 'An I'll breake mine if she die o' tha pewmonia.' say his missis.

* * *

"Thet wor a sure thing their little ow mawther coun't hev booth, an without they staarved theirselves on Chrissmas Day she coun't hev neither. Thet ent right a father should hatta chuse betwixt mearkin his child warm, meakin thet happy, or feed in his family. Dick set thare garpin at narthin for a bit, an then he say, 'She'll git em,' he say. 'She'll git har bewts an har doll as well. She'll git em if I hatta steal em.'

"Corse, he never meant thet about stealin em. Pearple hed more pride than money in them days. Now they're got more money than pride. No, what he done wor go an see Arnie Carpenter.

" 'Arnie,' he say, 'I reckon things are as bad along o' yew as what they are along o' me.'

" 'They coun't be a lot wuss,' say Arnie. 'Tha paarson keep hevin his bewts mended when they dornt want dewin, an I carnt tell him diffrent, but besides him an tha gentry I dornt git enough customers to keep me in leather.'

"They mardled for a time, an in tha finish Arnie agreed to mearke Dick's kiddy a pair of bewts if Dick mearde Arnie's little ow dorter a doll.

"Dick went hoom an got hold o' some bits o' wood an clorth, an begged a bit o' pearnt orf o' a builder and mearde two dolls, one for his own dorter an one for Arnie's. They wornt much, but they wor better'n narthin.

*   *   *

"Corse, Dick wornt tha only feller what wanted bewts an toys for his young un. What he dint know wor that young Peter Bull hed orfered to mearke a wooden hoss for Arnie's son in exchearnge for a pair o' bewts, an Ned Cutch wor dewin tha searme sort o' trearde with a doll's house.

"Arnie Carpenter wor thet sorft-harted he coun't never say no, an tha narer they got to Chrissmas, tha more an more toys kept stackin theirselves up in Arnie's shud, an tha more an more bewts he kept a-mearkin for harf tha kids in tha willage. His missis mobbed him about it more'n once, reckonin he give more thowt to other pearple than what he done to his own family, but he told her, he say, if! dorn't keep on mearkin bewts I shall forgit my craaft.

"Arnie went up to tha Hall one mornin to see to tha ow squire's huntin-bewts. Them gentry'd go huntin ifthet wor Judgement Day. He took one o' them dolls along with him, cos thet wor jest like Arnie to want to give thet as a present to tha ow squire's dorter.

"Tha minnit she see thet thare doll, tha ow squire's wife arst Arnie whare he got it. 'Thass such a pretty little thing,' she say, 'an I want some presents to give to tha children's horspital.' Well, Arnie never told har whare thet come from, but he did say he'd got plenty more if she wanted em. 'I could dew with sellin em' he say, 'cos I're got tew many for my own kids, an I'll hatta git some money from somewhare dew I on't hev no leather by this time next week.'

"He nearmed his price, an from what I'm told he must a took har thutty or more toys of all sorts.

"On tha Chrissmas Eve, tha coach left tha Hall an went to tha children's horspital with a load o' toys. Then when thet come back thet went all round Dumpton leavin presents for tha willage. I dorn't know how they sorted them present out up at tha Hall, but all them toys what tha fathers hed mearde for Arnie Carpenter come back inter their own hooms. Some got tha werra ones they'd mearde theirselves, but moost got them what other fellers hed mearde. Thet wor like as if Peter Bull hed swopped his wooden hoss for Ned Cutch's doll's house an so on an so forth.

* * *

"Now thass a rummun when yew think on it. They all got their bewts for their kids, and they all got toys an to spare, and Arnie Carpenter got his money. What I want to know is, who paid for it?"

"Nobra dint pay for em," say tha boy Chaarlie. "they might as well a mearde them things an spreed em around among theirselves."

"Then how would Arnie Carpenter a got his money?" arst Ow Dan. "Alright, then," say Fred Johnson, "tha Hall paid for em."

"Oh, no, thet never." say Ow Dan. "I'll tell yew who paid for em. Whare did tha Hall git tha money from? From tha tenents. Who wor tha tenents? Tha farmers. Whare did tha farmers git tha money from? From tha sweat o' us learbourers. Us learbourers paid for all them things, an a lot more beside what we never got sight nor feel on."

Ow Dan helped hisself to a pint o' mild what Tom Drew hed jest drored for Enoch Fletcher. "Ah," he say, "thare's plenty o' money about today, an thare'd a bin plenty about yares ago if thet'd a gorn inter tha pockets o' them what arned it. What pearple want to remember in 1960, as much as in 1890, is whare thet come from."

HARBERT
1st January, 1960

HARBERT AND ALICE IN LONDON
FOR THE WEDDDING

Harbert "slept rough" last Thursday night, having gone up to London with his wife to join the Royal wedding crowds in The Mall. Of course, he was reluctant to go, but glad in the end, that he did. And so are we – for the sake of this exclusive eye-witness account of a great occasion. – Editor

"Yew may not want to see tha weddin," say tha Gal Alice, "but I dew, an whass more, I'm a-goin tew."

"Lor, more," I say, "all tha money we shall hull away gittin to London an back, we could hev a proper holiday at Yarmouth."

"Thass what yew telled me larst yare," she say, "and I never got no holiday at all. Well, thet ent a-goin to happen t'yare. I'm mearkin sure o' gittin one holiday time I can. I'm a-goin to London to see Princess Margaret's weddin, an yew're a-comin tew."

"Tha marster woun't never give me tha day orf," I say.

"Oh yes, he will" she say. "I arst him."

"We carnt leave tha twins," I say.

"Oh yes, we can," she say. "My Ma'll hev em."

* * *

Well, yew carnt argew with wimmen, can yer? So thass how we come to fetch up in London at some rum ow hour on tha Tharsda night, an arter a lot o' muckin about we got tew a plearce called tha Maul.

My hart, thet wor a maul an all. Yew should a sin tha pearple! Moost on em wor farmers, I reckon, cos thare wor a lot o' posh cars. Thet wor long parst bed-time for any respeckable feller, but thare must a bin thousands on em a-jammin up an down.

"Coo," say tha gal Alice, "look at all them banners with tha bride an bridegroom's inishals on!"

"Banners," I say. "They look like bedspreads. I'm orf."

She say, "Whare dew yew reckon yew're a-goin?"

I say, "I'm goin to bed. This hare weddin ent till tomorrer."

"Bed!" she shruck. "Hev yew gorn light? Who dew yew reckon's goin to give yew a bed at this time o' night? Now we're hare, hare's whare we're a-goin to stay till tha bride come parst."

"Is thet why yew mearde me carry all these hare coats an rugs?" I say. "Dew I'd a known, I'd a hulled em out o' tha trearn winder."

"Well, hull yew them down on this hare bit o' pearvement instead," she say, "betwixt thet fat woman with tha squint an them mawthers in britches with their hair hangin down their backs like I dornt know what."

* * *

I coun't dew much else, could I? I hulled them rugs down an she spreeded them out, an I sat down next to them mawthers.

"Not thet side," say tha gal Alice. "Set yew next to thet fat woman with tha squint."

"Hello," say this hare woman.

"Dew yew know har?" I say to tha gal Alice. "I hent never sin her afore, but she jest spook to me."

"Dornt tearke no notice," say tha gal Alice.

"Whare dew yew come from?" arst this hare woman.

"Dumpton," I say.

"Whare's thet?" she say.

"My hart, mor," I say. "Yew dornt know much, dew yer?"

Then them mawthers in britches tarned on some sort o' grammerfone an got up an staarted darncin this hare rotten roll.

I say to tha gal Alice, I say "We ent a-goin to git a lot o' sleep hare," I say.

An nor we dint. Howsomever, thet wor alright arter tha sun come up an tha gal Alice got out a bottle o' cold tea an some cheese sanwiches an pickled onions, an this hare fat woman what hed laid on my foot harf tha night got up an shook harself, an I got up an hopped about on tha other foot to git rid o' tha pins an needles, an all them banners an flowers an things looked a treart.

Then more policemen than what I're ever sin together at one time, an hope I never dew see agin, lined theirselves up all over tha shop.

"They're lookin for somebodda," I say.

"Hold yar tongue dew," say tha gal Alice.

"What dew they look like?" I say. "These hare London police carnt a hed any new uniforms for I dornt know how long. Why our P.C. Bumble ent dressed as old-fashuned as them."

"Shut yew up," say tha gal Alice. "Thass what they call their dress uniforms."

"Then thass time they hed new uns," I say. "I're sin Chaarlie Chaplin wear things like them in tha silent fillums."

* * *

Corse them on hosses looked alright. Some o' them hosses wor a duzzy site better than any what yew see at Flitmarsh pint-to-pint. One or tew wor a bit gaily, but them cops knew how to handle em.

Then we hud a brarss band a-comin, an tha Gards come marchin up. They're a smaart lot o' men they are, with their red coats an big ow black things like heartrugs on their hids. Their orficers staarted a-hollerin like bookies an they all jumped about. They arn their money.

Tha gal Alice wor gittin right excited an I might a bin if thet thare fat woman hent a hed har full weart on my foot agin, when all of a sudden tha cars staarted comin down from Buckinham Pallace, with all tha big nobs for tha weddin. All kinds o' flags they hed on tha front, an men in top hats inside. Yew see cars like them drored up outside tha Red Lion when thare's a Farmers' Union dinner on, but yew dornt see so many. Thare wor hunderds on em one arter tha other, an tha gal Alice kept on a-jumpin up an down sharmin out: "Look, thare's Sir Winston Charchill, look! Thare's Sir Anthony Eden, look! Coo, look, look, thare he be, thass him, look!"

"Him? Who?" I say.

"Him, tha bridegrume. Tony Armstrong-Jones!" she say. "Oh dew look at him," she say, "dornt he look narvous!"

"Narvous?" I say. "If I wor him, I'd be putrified."

But she hent hardly got over thinkin he smiled right at har when, "Ooooh!" she hollered, "look at them come hare!" an tha finest sight I ever did see in my life come canterin down tha rood. Hosses, big ow black uns with a touch o' white on tha hid, comin fower by fower an tha men a-ridin on em fared to look as if they'd bin set on fire. Greart ow silver armer on their chests they hed, what ketched tha sun an shone like our charch winder on a fine Sunday in July. Plumes on their hids bobbed up an down an as they went parst they jingled like a sack o' soverins. An arter them come tha Queen.

* * *

She wor ridin in a coach like what yew see in kids' picksher-books, an she wearved har hand at us as she went by, an we wearved back at har. She hed on a blew dress, an tha Queen Mother wor alongside har in white, an Prince Chaarles wor all dressed up like a young Scotchman, an he wor a-jumpin about in thet thare coach enough to give his mother a fit. But she never say narthin, she jest kept a-smilin an a-wearvin, an I reckon she must hev a lot more pearshience with har young uns than what I're got with mine.

She wor parst in a flash, an tha gal Alice wor singin out: "Hare come tha bride! Oh Harbert, ent this lovely! I wonder what har weddin-dress look like!"

"If thet look as big a treart to Armstrong-Jones as what yars did to me," I say, "then thass a good un."

"Oh, Harbert," she say, "why carnt yew say things like thet when I're got time to lissen? Look, look, hare she come! Oh dew look at thet coach!"

Mind yew, I ent sayin tha coach what tha Queen went in wornt pretty, but this hare one what tha Princess wor in wor a lot prettier. Thet wor sort o' smaller, an as thet come up thet put me in mind of a cearge with a white bud a-flutterin inside it.

"Ooooh ent she lovely!" sung out tha gal Alice. "An har dress! An them jewls a-glitterin in har hair! No bride coun't look prettier, not if she tried. An my hart if she dint hatta git har hankercher out an dab har glimmers.

What with this fat woman a-howlin one side an tha gal Alice a-howlin tha other, I fared to feel a proper fewl. But I must say if I hent a bin a man I'd a bin a-howlin along with em, cos thare's allers suffin what sort o tarn yar hart over about seein a young woman on har way to har weddin, an when thet thare young woman charnce to be a Princess, an look right down pretty inter tha bargin, I dornt care who yew are, yew're a duzzy liar if yew say yew dornt feel narthin.

* * *

Well, we hud him an har say "I will" over tha loudspeakers, an we stood thare till they come back agin, an tha wimmen wornt a-howlin this time, they wor on tip-toe a-hollerin.

"Oh, Harbert," say tha gal Alice, "dornt they look happy?"

"Well, mor," I say, "if he're gorn an got hisself as good a wife as what

84

I hev, he're got suffin to be happy about."

"Harbert!" she say, "yew carnt go sayin things like thet thare about a Princess!"

"Well, thass right enough, ent it?" I say.

"I dornt know," she say. "But I hope he's as good a husband to har as what yew are to me."

HARBERT

13th May, 1960

BRANDY AN' POLISH

Thare wornt nobra in tha Fox but Tom Drew, the landlord, when P. C. Bumble drollerched in arter dinner larst Tewsda, He dropped a handful o' wheat on tha counter, give Tom a look an say, "Whadda yew mearke o' this hare."

"Thass wheat," say Tom.

"I know thass wheat," say Bumble. "I ent sorft! But whass thet bin soaked in? Dew yew smell it."

Tom stuck a bit under his snout an sniffed.

"Thet smell like brandy," he say.

"Is thet yar expart opinion?" arst Bumble. "Cos if so I might be callin on yew as an expart wirness. Then agin, if yew're in this hare as deep as what I think, yew might not be a witness at all. Yew might be suffin else." An he give Tom another funny ow look.

* * *

"What tha hike are yew a-runnin on about?" arst Tom.

"This hare wheat what smell o' brandy," say Bumble, "when did Humpty Potter larst buy a bottle o' brandy orf o' yew?"

"He dornt never buy no brandy orf o' me," say Tom.

"Thass what I thowt," say Bumble. "Or as yew might say, tha facks all point to tha bewt bein on tha other foot."

"Are yew suggestin…?" arst Tom.

85

"Suggestin?" say Bumble. "Now what mearke yew think I'm suggestin suffin? All I'm sayin is I picked this hare wheat up on Ow Mother Quail's – I mean Mrs Quail's land. My next dewty is to find out how thet got thare."

"Well, thare ent much mistry about thet," say Tom. "Thass one o' tha oldest tricks thare is. Somebodda what want to ketch Ow Mother Quail's pheasants a bin soakin this hare wheat in brandy an layin thet whare they'll pick thet up. Then when they git sozzled all he're gotta dew is lang hold on em an hull em inter his sack."

"Ah," say Bumble.

"I spose yew think thass Humpty Potter what done it," say Tom. "Well, all I can say is, what yew want to dew is ketch him with tha pheasants on him."

"I ent innerested in tha pheasants," say Bumble, stickin his snout about an inch from Tom's.

"Then what are yew innerested in?" hollered Tom.

"I'm innerested in tha brandy," say Bumble. "Pheasants ent not narthin, but brandy's a diffrent thing altogether. We're bin gettin reports about smuggling goin on along tha coast. Thet woun't surprise me to larn Potter is mixed up in it. An if he is, thet woun't surprise me to larn he're got a good customer for some on it on his own doorstep."

"I ent tearkin thet lyin down," sung out Tom.

"Lyin down or standin up, I dornt know what yew're gittin riled about," say Bumble. "I dint menshun yar nearme, did I?"

"No, an yew'd best not," say Tom.

"Well, then," say Bumble.

I ent sayin Tom Drew give Humpty tha wink, an I ent sayin he dint, but when Bumble stuck his bike up agin Humpty's front porch an banged on tha door, Humpty wor out.

"Now's my charnce to see inside his shud," Bumble say to hisself, an in he went.

"Ah," he say, "an whass this hare might I arst?" he say, as he ketched sight of a bottle stood on a chest o' drawers. "Learbel in furrin writin, some sort o' dark liquid inside. Now we're gettin a bit fudder."

* * *

He wor jest a-goin to pull tha cork out when Humpty come up behind him. "Stick em up!" say Humpty.

"Dornt act sorft, Potter," say Bumble, as he stuck his hands up.

"My hart alive, if thet ent Bumble." say Humpty. "Yew want to be careful tha way yew go round brearkin inter pearple's property. I might a shot yer. Well dornt stand thare with yar hands up like a duzzy fewl. I hent got a gun."

Bumble tarned round an wearved tha bottle. "Whare's tha rest on it, Potter?" he say.

"Rest o' what?" arst Humpty.

"Yew know as well as what I dew," say Bumble. "Tha brandy."

"What a yew got a tharst on?" say Humpty.

"I dornt want none o' yar lip," say Bumble. "I hev reason to believe yew're mixed up in smugglin, an if yew give cheeky arnsers thet'll go agin yer in court."

"Hev yew gorn light?" arst Humpty.

"I'm warnin yew Potter," say Bumble. "Yew may a slipped parst tha law afore, but yew ent a-goin to git away with this lot. From informearshun reseeved, tha stuff in this hare bottle a bin comin in illegal up along tha coast an findin its way inland in contrawenshun o' tha regulearshuns. Now whare is it?"

"Thet ent brandy in thet thare bottle," say Humpty. "Thass French polish."

"Thass French alright," say Bumble, "but thet ent polish. Whass this hare on tha learbel – C-O-G-N-A-C?"

"Thass tha French for polish," say Humpty.

"I know diffrent to thet," say Bumble. "I wor in France in tha war."

"I reckon thass why thet took so long to win," say Humpty.

* * *

"I'm tellin yew for tha larst time, Potter," say Bumble. "I dornt want none o' yar lip. Whare wor yew when I got hare?"

"In charch," say Humpty.

"Thet settle it," say Bumble. "French polish. In charch. Yew're done it for yarself this time, Potter. I allers did say yew'd be impartinent once tew orfen. Open this hare bottle."

Humpty opened tha bottle an Bumble took a sniff.

"Satisfied?" arst Humpty.

"No, thet I ent," say Bumble. "Give me thet thare glarss."

Humpty give him tha glarss an he poured a bit out. He tipped thet inter his gob an rolled thet round, but afore he could swaller it his fearce went skarlet an he let out a roar.

"Aaaarrrggghh!" he shruck as he spat thet out. "Warnish!"

"I're hud o' some rum things in my time," say Humpty. "I're hud o' ow tramps drinkin methilearted spirrits, but I hent never hud of a policeman gittin a cravin for French polish afore. I dornt know as how I dint oughter tell yar inspeckter."

* * *

Bumble got on his bike an mizzled orf with his stummick tarnin over. I'll say this hare for Bumble, he think quick. Thet wornt more'n harf-n-hour arterwards when suffin struck him.

"In charch," he say to hisself, "Praps he meant it. Praps thare's more in this hare than what meet tha eye. Thet woun't dew no haarm for me to go an talk to tha paarson."

He got a shock at tha Wicaridge alright, but I'll hatta leave thet till next time.

HARBERT
3rd February, 1961

BOTTLE IN THE BELFRY

Tha Wicar hed his snout in Foxe's Book o' Marters when P.C. Bumble rung his bell.

"Ah, Constable," he say. "Wipe yar bewts on tha mat as yew come in. What can I dew for yew?"

"Thass like this hare, Reverend," say Bumble. "I'm parsewin my inquiries inter whare Cornelius Potter, what they call Humpty, git his brandy from."

"Surely yew dornt think he git it from me?" say tha Wicar.

"Ha, ha! No, sartainly not, Reverend. Ha, ha!" say Bumble.

"Then how can I help?" arst tha Wicar. "Hev Potter took to drink?

I carnt say I're notised him being tha warse for drink, not more than usual."

*   *   *

"Thet ent a question o' drink, Reverend," say Bumble. "Thass a question o' smugglin." An he telled tha Wicar moost o' what I telled yer larst week, only thet took him twice tha time an he left out tha bits what mearde him look a fewl.

"So yew see," he wound up, "I thowt thet my dewty to arst yew what Potter meant by sayin he'd bin in tha charch."

"Dare me," say tha Wicar, rubbin his glarsses with his handkercher. "Extrordinry. But tha fack is Potter DID go to tha charch this arternune."

"Ah," say Bumble. "Might I arst for why?"

"Why, bless my soul, Potter's not such a rarscal as what he's pearnted," say tha Wicar. "We all know he's a bit of a poacher, an I carnt deny he's a mite shaarp at times, but he hev a good hart, a good hart."

"Oh hev he," say Bumble. "Then I've yit to see it."

"Nonsense," say tha Wicar. "If others wor as willin to give up their time to parform little sarvices for tha charch as what Potter is, this hare parrish'd be better than what thet is."

*   *   *

"I'll lay tha only time Potter ever went inter a charch thet wor to nick tha brarsses," say Bumble, "or tha pore-box."

"Pore-box?" say tha Wicar. "Thare hent been narthin in our pore-box for a twelve-month. No, yew dew Potter a grearve injustice. Why, this larst week or tew, in what spare time he hev, he're bin woluntarily puttin a bit of a shine on tha pews. They wor gittin in a sad stearte, them pews. Old as tha hills, moost on em. They're bin needin a warnish I dornt know how long."

"Warnish!" sharmed out Bumble.

"Sartainly," say tha Wicar. "I spose Potter wor tha natcheral man for tha job, in a way. Arter all, among tha many things what he deal in, he hev a lot to dew with farnitcher. Thare's allers a bit o' warnish on his premmises. As yew know, he lay in old farnitcher from tha searles, shine thet up, an sell thet again at a profit. So when he orfered to restore tha pews, I accepted gladly. Little by little, week by week, he're bin mearkin em look like new. He done a bit this arternune."

"Did yew see him?" arst Bumble.

"I see him arrive," say tha Wicar. "I wor in tha charch myself when he come in an dumped some more o' his bottles o' warnish or French polish, or whatever he call it, in tha belfry. I never knew thet took so much warnish to cover a few pews till I see Potter at wark."

* * *

Bumble give him a look. "How much warnish dew he use?" he arst.

"Well, this arternune I should think he browt in a couple o' dozen bottles," say tha Wicar. "He come rushin in in a tearin hurry an put em down with tha rest in tha belfry. Pore feller, he dornt git a lot o' time for his noble wark. Rush in an rush out, thass how he dew."

"What dew yew mean, Reverend, with tha rest?" arst Bumble. "How many o' them bottles a bin lyin about in tha belfry at one time?"

"Ah, now, yew may well arst," say tha Wicar. "Quite a number I should say, quite a number. But I never interfare with a crarftsman in executin his dewty. They lay out o' sight in a daark corner, so I carnt complearn o' their bein a newsance."

He wor a-goin to say suffin else, but all of a sudden he stopped an stood numcharnce. "Surely yew dornt think…" he say.

"I dornt think narthin, Reverend," say Bumble, "but I reckon yew an me hed best go an hev a look at them bottles."

* * *

Thet wor daark in thet thare ow belfry when they got thare. Bumble shone his light about, an tha Wicar told him to point thet under an ow bier in tha far corner. "Thass whare he keep em," he say. "Thare's some rags an a brush as well. An there's…hold yew haard…they're gorn! Tha rags an tha brush are hare, but thare ent no bottles!"

Bumble sung out a couple o' wards what tha Wicar pretended not to hare.

"Beggin yar paarden, Reverend," he say, "but thass like I thowt. Thet all fit in. Potter a bin actin as middle-man for them smugglers. They're bin a-sendin him tha brandy, an he're bin a-storin on it in yar belfry. He must a known I wor arter him this arternune, so he come runnin up hare with tha larst lot what wor on his premmises. Then when I wor out o' tha way, back he come an git rid on it afore I can git round hare an find it. Thare's no tellin whare thet is now. I'll lay if I sarched his plearce from top to bottom I won't find...Hey, hang on a minnit. Whass this hare a-flashin whare my light shine on it?"

Tha Wicar bent down under tha bier agin an come up with a bottle.

"Bless my soul," he say. "I never spotted it."

"Nor did Potter," say Bumble an his ow glimmers shone. "He missed it! He left one behind! Now we're got him!"

* * *

Tha Wicar rubbed his glarsses an took a peark at tha learbel.

"What did I tell yer!" say Bumble. "I hent bin to collidge, but I can read French enough to know thass brandy in thet thare bottle. I want yew to look at thet careful, Reverend, cos yew might hatta testify in due corse. Dew thet say brandy on tha learbel or dornt it?"

"Thet sartainly seem to," say tha Wicar, a bit flummoxed.

"Alright, then," say Bumble, "I'm glad now thet wornt brandy I found in his shud. This hare's a lot better, cos I're got a independent witness. I'll tearke fust swig."

He whinged tha cork out an took a pull at tha bottle.

He stood thare for a second an then let out a yell what mearde tha bell ring.

"Aaaaarrrggghh!" he shruck. "Warnish! Weart till I git my hands on Potter! He done it o' parpose!"

Thet dint carm him down a lot when tha Wicar say, "Ater all, Constable. I must remind yew that I did tell yew thet wor warnish what Potter browt inter tha belfry."

Me. I ent sayin one thing nor yit tha other, but if yew want to keep a drop o' brandy agearnst sickness, yew can git some good stuff from Tom Drew a bit cheaper than what yew would in Flitmarsh.

HARBERT
10th February, 1961

DAY AT THA REARCES

Tha marster give us a lift in his lorry to tha Flitmarsh Pint-to-Pint. Corse, thet brook down harfway. Tha marster an tha boy Willie stuck their skulls in tha injin an diddled about for a harf-an-hour.

Tha gal Alice say to me, she say, "I might as well git out an pick some flowers."

"Lor mor," I say, "thare ent no flowers what I can see."

"Thet dornt matters," she say, "I're got some seeds."

* * *

Time we set thare a feller come parst leadin a hoss. We hully did larf at him. Thet wor a totty little ow hoss what fared to look like thet'd a fell down dew he'd a took tha harness orf.

"Thet thare hoss is a rum ow job, ent it?" sung out Enoch Fletcher. "What dew yew reckon yew're a-goin to dew with it?"

"I'm a-goin to rearce it," say this feller.

"Dew yew arst me, bor," say Enoch, "yew'll beat it."

Howsomever, we got thare in tha finish, an thass a good job we wor learte, cos our lorry being larst in, thet wor fust out. Thare wor thet many cars an lorries in thet there fild yew coun't see narthin for mud.

"Go yew on, gal Alice," I say, "Jump yew down an tell me how deep thet is."

"My hart alive," she say, "yew domt want much, dew yer? Thass tha man's plearce to git down an' tell his wife how deep thet is"

Time we wor argifyin young Rupert larnshed hisself orf tha lorry an we hud him holler.

Enoch Fletcher pearked over tha side an we say "How deep in is he?"

"Up tew his ankles," say Enoch.

"He's alright then," I say.

"I dornt know so much," say Enoch, "he went in skull-fust." Corse, he only say thet for a larf.

We wor alright once we did git down, cos thet there mud wornt as deep as what thet looked.

On our way to see tha rearces tha gal Alice lorst one o' har shoes. I got myself plarstered with mud from hid to foot sarchin for it, an she hully did mob me cos' I coun't find it. Then I went an got a stick an prooged about for it, an when I did find it she sharmed out, "This hare ent mine. Thass a right foot an I lorst a left!"

"Thet must be yars, mor," I say. "I reckon yew must a got tew right feet."

"We'll hatta sign har up as centre-forrard for tha Wanderers," say Enoch.

Tha gal Alice wore hully riled, so I kept a-lookin. Then a woman came lumpin up with a shoe on har left foot an narthin on har right. "Thet must be my shoe what yew're got thare," she say.

"Howd yew hard a minnit," I say. "Yew're got one pair betwixt tha tew on yer now" I say, "so tha best thing yew can dew is toss up for it."

Corse they woun't hev thet, but ow Enoch like a bit of a larf, so he got a harf-a-crown out o' his pocket an say: "Thass tha only fair way to settle it," he say. "Dew yew call, gal Alice" he say, "Hids or tearls." An he spun tbet thare harf-a-crown up in tha air.

I might a told him what'd happen. He missed thet comin down an thet fell right on to tha mud. Thet lay thare winkin at him for a second an then thet sunk.

"Yew duzzy ow fewl, yew," shruck his missis, "now yew're gorn an lorst a harf-a-crown."

"Oh no, I hent" say Enoch, "I'll find thet if I hatta stay here till Mickelmas."

So he took his coat orf and staarted diggin about, and tha way he went at it we wor all plarstered with mud, tha wimmen an all, afore yew could say Jack Robinson. He dint find his harf-a-crown, but he found tha gal Alice's shoe, an tha larst we see on him he wor burrerin like a duzzy rabbit with his ow woman a-mobbin on him.

* * *

Then we come to whare all them-thare bookies wor a-hollerin, and thet thare thing what they call tha teetotal-isator stood thare. Tha hosses wor a-goin round the ring gittin ready for that Flitmarsh Hunt Cup, so 1 say to tha gal Alice, I say, "What dew'yew fancy?"

She say, "I fancy a cup of tea," she say.

"No," I say, "what hoss?"

"Look at thet thare Mrs. Hogtrott from Fumbleham," she say. "Did yew ever see such a hat as what she're got on?"

"I dint come hare to look at tha hats," 1 say.

"Well, I dint come hare to look at tha hosses," she say. "I can see hosses out o' my kitchen winder."

"I fancy thet thare bay belongin to Captin Fulsom-Frortb," I say, "an if I look smaart I'll jest hev time to stick a bob on it."

So I got out my little ow parse what I keep my munny in when I'm out.

"Thass a rummun, mor," I say. "Afore we come away thare wor ten shillin in hare,"

"Thass right," say tha gal Alice.

"Well, thet ent thare now," I say.

"No," say tha gal Alice, "thet ent, is it?"

"I carn't a lorst it,"I say.

"Yew hent," say tha gal Alice, "But yew would a done dew I hent a' took thet out an stuck thet under tha clock on tha mantelpiece."

"Lor, mor," I say, "I carnt bet on a hoss without I're got tha money."

"Thass what I reckoned," say tha gal Alice.

"But I won fower-an-a-tanner larst yare," I say.

"Yew wornt married larst yare," say tha gal Alice. "Now yew are."

Well, I coun't dew narthin, could I? Tha gal Alice reckoned she dint mind me goin an watchin tha rearces, but if I wanted a cup o' tea I'd hatta stick along o' har cos she's got tha munny. Arter tha second rearce she give me a bob to go an hev a glass o' beer along o' tha boy Willie.

* * *

Thare wore a funny ow crowd round where they wor a-sellin tha beer, an I war in tha middle on it when I felt suffin pull my coat, and when I tarned round thare wor a feller runnin orf
with my parse.

I thowt to myself, "Yew may run ow paartner, thare ent narthin in it." I wor jest a-goin to larf when I remembered thet thare parse corst munny, so I run arter him. I lorst sight on him for a bit, but then I ketched him round tha back o' tha teetotal-isator.

I grabbed hold o' my parse, an when he staarted to kick up a row, I say, "Yew want to hold yar duller, dew I'll call a policeman," I say, "This hare parse a got my nearme in it."

He see he wor done, so he left me holdin tha parse an mizzled orf like Ow Nick wor arter hin.

I stuck thet back in my pocket, but thet fared to feel thicker, so I pearked inside an my hart if thare wornt tew pound fower shillin in it. Thet must a bin munny what thet thare thief hed on him.

"Sarve yew right, bor," I say. "Yew're paid a tew pound fine an fower shill in corsts,"

I din't know what to dew with thet thare munny for tha best, an in tha finish I stuck some on it on Gallopin Princess in tha Leardies Rearce at fower to one.

I ent saying how much I won, an o' corse I dussn't say narthin to tha gal Alice, but I took har to Flitmarsh on tha Saturda an bowt har tew pair o' shoes.

HARBERT
7th April, 1961

A-FIXIN' A FIGHT

What put thet inter tha boy Chaarlie's hid I dornt know. Some reckon thet wor them boxin matches what they're staarted runnin in Flitmarsh, an some say thet wor all thet money what they keep payin Floyd Patterson an tha Swede for knockin one another down.

All I know is, tha boy Chaarlie an young Bartie Tarner ketched hold o' Jack Vardle, him what they call Limpsy Vardle, an telled him he could mearke a forchune as a heavyweart.

"Is thet right?" arst Limpsy

"Corse thass right," say tha boy Chaarlie. "Stroppin greart feller like yew. Yew're got gold in them thare fists."

Young Limpsy opened his fists an took a good peark at his parms, but he coun't see no gold. All he could see wor harf a stoon o' mowld orf o' tha marster's ten-acre, cos he'd just bin digging a drearn.

"Besides," say Bartie Tarner, "yew dornt fear narthin, dew yer, Limpsy?"

Limpsy's greart big rosy red fearce split in tew an showed a grin like a semeterry. "Only spiders," he say. "I dornt like ow spiders."

95

"Thass alright then," say Chaarlie. "They woun't git yer to fight no spiders."

* * *

What else they telled him I carnt say, but tha nexter mornin I see Limpsy runnin up tha Diddlin' rood with a skippin-roop, an afore tha week wor out thet wor one o' tha sights o' tha willage to nip round an watch Limpsy shadder-boxin in his back yaard.

"Yew dornt know what yow're done," I say to tha boy Chaarlie, "Once he git thet inter his hid he's a boxer, thare ent no tellin whare he'll end up."

"He might be good at it," say Chaarlie. "He weigh fowerteen stoon odd, and he're got a kick like a mule."

"He's shanny," I say. "He're got a tile missin. He's half-rocked."

"Yew're gotta be to tearke up perfeshunal boxin," say Chaarlie.

"He're got tha mussel," I say, "but he ent above five foot high. He'd be fightin fellers o' six-foot-six."

"Well, they'd hatta bend down to hit him, woun't they?" say Chaarlie. "An when they bent down he could ketch em on tha snout."

* * *

I dint think no more about it. Arter a week or tew, so I reckoned, thet'd all die down. But I got a bit of a shock when one night I wor settin in tha Fox, an in come tha boy Chaarlie an telled us as young Limpsy wor on tha next bill at Flitmarsh. His fearce wor as white as a sheet.

"Thet ent my dewin," he say, "nor yit Bartie's. We only put tha idea in Limpsy's hid for a larf."

"Yew want shewtin, tha pair on yer," say Enoch Fletcher. "Who's he fightin?"

"A feller called Bob Rush from Ticklin Saint Andrew," say Chaarlie. "They're both mearkin their fust apparence in tha ring."

"Thet'll be Limpsy's larst apparence an all, if I know Bob Rush," say Fred Johnson. "He'll kill him."

"Bob Rush?" say Tom Drew, tha landlord. "I know Bob Rush. He're jest come out o' tha Army, hent he? He's tha feller what they dischaarged for tyin knots in tha rifles."

"Thass him," say Fred. "He's warkin for Tucker. He hit a cow larst Frida an that ent expected ter recover."

Enoch Fletcher up an stuck his snout about harf-an-inch from the boy Chaarlie's. "All I can say is," he say, "yew an thet fewl Bartie Tarner got young Limpsy inter this, an now yew'll hatta git him out."

* * *

Thet wor all werra well Enoch putting tha responsabilita on Chaarlie, but tha more we looked at it, tha more we come round to thinkin we'd all hatta swing together. I mean to say, tha honner o' Dumpton wor consarned. Thet wor out o' tha question to git Limpsy to call thet orf, cos we dint want Ticklin St. Andrew lookin down their snouts an sayin Dumpton fellers wor chicken. An another thing, accordin to what we could mearke out, Limpsy must a put his maark on a contrack.

I ent a feller to brag, as yew know, but this I will say, when I put my mind to suffin, thet ent orfen I'm beat. This hare bisness o' tha contrack staarted me orf thinkin. Arter I'd spook to a feller at Fumbleham what know a mawther whose sister's husban wor friendly with a boxer, I begun to see a bit o' daylight.

"This hare contrack o' Limpsy's," I told em in tha Fox a couple o' nights arter, "thass tha thing we're gotta wark on. Now yew may not know it – thet ent everybodda what dew – but them boxers' contracks are like this hare. If one feller stay away tha other feller git all tha money, so long as he's at tha ringside all ready to fight if he's wanted."

* * *

Thare wornt a deen for a minnit, ceptin a kind o' bubblin sound what might a bin Enoch's pipe an might a bin tha boy Chaarlie's mind a-warkin.

Then Fred Johnson say, "What yew mean, boy Harbert," he say, "is we're gotta mearke sure Bob Rush dornt tarn up, then Limpsy can clearm tha money."

"Can yew think o' suffin better?" I say.

"No, thet I carnt," say Fred.

"Then thass settled," say tha boy Chaarlie, an for tha next five minnits nobodda spook cos we all hed our snouts in our glarsses.

Enoch Fletcher wor tha fust to breark tha silence. "Hold yew on a minnit," he say. "Narthin ent settled yit. Hare's Harbert say we're gotta keep Bob Rush from tarnin up, but he never did say how he reckon we're a-goin to dew it."

Yew know when yew go inter a cow-shud all tha cows tarn round an look at yer? Well thass how they all tarned round an garped at me. I spose they reckoned I woun't know what to arnser. To speak tha honest trewth, they wornt far out.

"Thass up to yew" I say, "Yew carnt expeck me to dew all tha thinkin."

Arter another couple o' pints, tha boy Chaarlie say, "We could kidnap him," he say ...

"I'd like to see yer try," say Tom Drew. "Thet'd tearke a rejiment o' soljers to kidnap Bob Rush, an then thare'd be a few missin believed killed."

"I'm a married man," say Fred Johnson. "I ent a-goin to risk my neck."

* * *

I'll say this hare for tha Fox, thass full o' noise and larfter as a rewle. That ent orfen yew see us lot set thare bitin our thumms, but thass what we done now. Howsomever, like I say, when I hatta think quick I can think quick, an thet wornt more'n harf an hour by tha clock afore I let out a holler.

"I're got it," I say. "Why is it we dornt want Limpsy to fight Bob Rush? Cos Bob Rush could mearke sossidge-meat on him, thass why. But come to think on it, Limpsy ent no witterer hisself. Sposin thet got round Ticklin Saint Andrew thet Limpsy hed harf killed bigger men than Rush? I reckon they'd want to call their man orf, searme as what we want."

"My hart, bor, yew're hit it," say Enoch. "Only I'd go one better. All we're gotta dew is git Limpsy's blood up an let him go trew Ticklin like a tempest."

"Thass warth a try," say Tom Drew.

Thet wor warth a try alright, but thet dint tarn out tha way we expected.

HARBERT
21st April, 1961

VARDLE v RUSH – FIGHT SPECIAL

We picked a night when we knew Bob Rush hed gorn to tha pickshers at Flitmarsh, an then six on us piled inter Fred Johnson's little ow fower-seater an nipped over to Ticklin Saint Andrew.

We brook a spring on tha way, cos we'd got Hundredweart Hodge, our blacksmith, in tha car, an him an young Limpsy Vardle weigh thutty-suffin stoon betwixt em.

Thet war a fine clare evenin, with tha sun a shinin an tha blackbuds an mavishes a-singin, as we pulled up outside tha Green Man.

"Right," say Fred Johnson, "yew know what yew're gotta dew, dornt yew, Limpsy?"

Limpsy puffed out his cheeks till his fearce fared to look like a copper kettle.

*   *   *

"Dew?" he say. "I hent got to dew narthin, hev I?"

"My hart alive," say Enoch Fletcher, "arter all tha time we're took to larn him."

"Yew're gotta act fierce, Limpsy," say tha boy Chaarlie. "Like a duzzy lion."

"I carnt roar," say Limpsy, "I're got a sor troot."

"Lor, bor, yew dornt hatta roar," say Fred. "Yew jest hatta look fierce, thass all."

"Frighten tha daylights out o' them Ticklin lot, thass all yew're gotta dew," say Enoch. "Like we showed yer at tha Fox. Thass why Hundredweart come with us, He's a-goin to show em some strong-man tricks, an then when they all see what a powerful feller he is, he's a-goin to pick a quarrel with yew, and then yew hit him an he fall down. Thet oughter larn em."

"Is thet right?" say Limpsy.

We took another few minnits refreshin Limpsy's memmery, if thass what yew can call it, an then we sarntered round to tha side door. Enoch remaarked thet he dint reckon thare'd be a lot o' pearple about, seeing as thet war fine an they'd all be dewin their gaardens, but when we maarched in we got a shock.

*   *   *

I reckon evera man an boy in Ticklin must a bin thare, an few o' tha wimmen as well. Tha plearce wor thick with smook, an like a hothouse, an tha row they wore kickin up put me in mind o' tha pig maarket at Flitmarsh on a Saturda.

We imitearted to barge trew tha crush but we dint git far, an Enoch war jest arstin a bald-hidded feller what all the hullabaloo wor about when I charnced to peark over somebodda's showlder an spot Humpty Potter in tha middle on it.

"Any more at ten to one?" sung out Humpty, wearvin a dutty little ow notebook an a stub o' pensil, an then I notissed thet moost o' tha crowd hed haarf-crowns, ten-bob notes, an even quid-notes in their hands.

"My hart, he's mearkin a book," say Enoch.

"I'll lay he's mearkin a book on tha fight," I say.

"Thass one thing we never took inter account" say Fred. "We dint never oughter a staarted on this hare without findin out what Humpty wor up tew."

"If they're all bettin on Bob Rush," say the boy Chaarlie, "thass a sure thing they on't mearke him call the fight orf now."

* * *

They talk about yar hart sinkin inter yar bewts, dornt they. Well I reckon mine must a garn clean trew tha floor inter tha seller. Somehow we mannidged to git nare tha bar an order a pint apiece, an then we stood thare tellin one another what we'd dew to Humpty when we got him back to Dumpton.

In tha finish Enoch say, "Well," he say, "we dint come hare for narthin. Thet on't dew no haarm to carry on as planned. At least thet'll give this Ticklin lot suffin to think about time we work out suffin else."

Thet wornt long afore tha bettin died down a bit, an Enoch staarted an argy-bargy with a ginger-haired feller about Bob Rush's charnces.

"Who is this hare Rush?" he say. "He hent bin in yar willage five minnits. All anybodda know about him is he left tha Army an come hare lookin for a job. We're got harf-a-dozen fellers at Dumpton what could twilt him good an proper with one hand behind their backs."

"Dornt be a duke's-hidded fewl," say this ginger feller. "Bob Rush could pick yew up an hull yew over his showlder with one finger."

We jined in on Enoch's side, an tha Ticklin lot backed up tha ginger feller, an thet wor beginning to hot up when some woman shruck, "Thass him!"

"Him? Who? Whare?" sung out them Ticklin crowd.

"Thet round red feller like a Dutch cheese with tha mumps," she hollered. "Thass young Vardle, what think he can beat Bob Rush."

* * *

They all garped at Limpsy like cats garpin at a goldfish, an Limpsy grinned fit to kill hisself. Then they all bust out larfin.

"Yew may larf," sharmed out Enoch, "but he's strong, this boy is. He's stronger than our blacksmith, an thass sayin suffin. Leardies an gennlemen, I want yew to meet Mr. Hodge, our blacksmith. With yar permishun I'm a-goin to arst Mr. Hodge to show yew some o' his feets o' strength, an when he're done yew'll git a oppertunity to see thet he ent narthin but a wittery ow woman compared with our young hope an fewcher warld champion, Jack Vardle."

I must say thet shut em up. They set thare like kids in Sunda skewl, weartin far tha show to staart, an I reckon we'd a stood a good chamce o' mearkin em think twice about Bob Rush if thet hent a bin for Humpty Potter.

He'd bin settin thare as silent as tha grearve all along, but afore Hundredweart could git his coat orf, he up an shook his fist at Limpsy an say: "Young Vardle yew're chicken!"

* * *

Thet wor suffin we dint never expect. I mean to say, yew dornt reckon to see a feller from yar own willage tarn agin yer. Limpsy dint know what to dew, cos we hent telled him. He give another grin, an staarted to hacker. "Is th-thet-r-r-right?" he say.

"I'll knock yar block orf for yew," say Humpty, an come walkin as slow as slow acrorst tha floor torrards Limpsy with one hand held out in front on him.

I're sin some rum things in my time, but if I live to be a hunderd, I on't never git over tha shock o' what happened next. One minnit Limpsy wor thare, tha next minnit he wornt. He jest let out a blood-cardlin howl, his hair stood up like a fild o' wheat, an he war out o' thet door afore yew could blink an eyelid.

"What did I tell yer?" say Humpty. "He's chicken."

Thare womt no sense us stopping, so we went. Tha larst thing I hud as I crept away wor a score o' fellers wantin to double their bets on Bob Rush, an Humpty tellin em he'd hatta shorten tha odds, but bein a honest feller he'd tearke their money.

* * *

We war harfway to Dumpton afore we ketched up with Limpsy.

"Yew fewl, yew," say Enoch. "what mearde yew run? Yew're done for us all now,"

"He hed a spider," howled Limpsy. "Thass like I telled yer, I carnt abide ow spiders."

All night thare wor suffin kept tellin me Humpty Potter wor actin proper peculiar. Harfway trew my breakfas I see thet in a flash. Orf I searled an fanged hold on him.

"Lor, bor," I say, "if Bob Rush win yew'll hev a tidy lot o' money to payout."

"If he win," say Humpty.

HARBERT
28th April, 1961

HARBERT REPORTS THE RINGSIDE DRAMA

Arter thet thare disarster at Ticklin Saint Andrew, thet took fower nights haard thinkin in the Fox to strearten ourselves out. Time an agin Tom Drew hed to tell us we'd rewin him if we dint stop talkin an staart drinkin.

Corse I dornt blearme Tom but thet thare boxin-match betwixt Limpsy Vardle an Bob Rush wanted some talkin about. I mean to say, as far as what we could see thare wor no way o' stoppin it.

I dornt want to mearke out I'm clever, thow if I telled yer I wor a fewl thet'd be a lie, but to be honest thet wor me what see daylight in tha finish.

* * *

"Lor," I say, at harf-arter-nine on the Tharsda night, "ent we a lot o'buzzlehids."

"Dew yew speak for yarself," say tha boy Chaarlie.

"We're hullin ourselves inter a buffle over narthin," I say. "Thare ent a-goin to be no fight an I'll tell yer for why. Cos Humpty Potter'll see to it Bob Rush never tarn up."

"I dornt git yar drift," say Enoch Fletcher.

"Then dew yew warsh yar lugs out an lissen," I say. "Humpty Potter a bin tearkin bets on Bob Rush all round tha districk. He must be holdin a mint o money. I know for a fack one faarmer at Diddlin Parva laid down twetty quid at ten to one, an scores more a bin bettin in tens an fives. But I hent hud o' nobodda wantin to bet a penny piece on Limpsy. So what dew that signify?"

"Thet signify a cold in tha hid for Humpty if Bob Rush win," say Fred Johnson.

"He'd stand to luse thousans," say Tom Drew.

"Well, then," I say.

"Well what?" arst tha boy Chaarlie.

"Did yew ever hare o' Humpty lusin thousans?" I say..

They all fanged hold o' their pint pots an hed a good swaller time they thowt thet over.

"Corse yew dint," I say, "an nor yit did I. Thet can only mean one thing. Humpty know if Bob Rush ever git in thet ring he'll marder Limpsy. So with all thet thare money in his pocket, he'll mearke thet his bisness to see Bob Rush never honner his contrack."

"What yew mean is," say Enoch Fletcher, "without us liftin a finger, thet'll be searfe enough for Limpsy to tarn up at tha ring all ready to box. Then when th M.C. holler for Bob Rush, he'll be missin, cos Humpty'll a paid him to stay away, an Limpsy'll git tha wardict an tha fee."

"I never said Humpty'd pay him to stay away," I say, "but tha rest on it is alright."

* * *

We felt a lot better in our minds arter thet. I might go so far as to say we felt cock-o-tha-walk. We hed a good larf together evera time we met, an we hed a bigger larf when we hud thare wor a rewmer goin round Ticklin thet Limpsy wor thet chicken he wornt a-goin to tarn up for tha fight.

We wor larfin all tha way to Flitmarsh tha night we took Limpsy along to this hare boxin tornament.

"Now they'll see if yew're a-goin to tarn up or not, Limpsy," we say, an he roared thet loud we hed to shut him up cos thet cracked Fred's windscreen.

We never went in tha boxers' entrance at tha back cos we knew Limpsey wornt a-goin to fight. We'd bought him a ringside seat along o' us so he could watch tha rest o' tha fights arter he'd collected his winnins. Streart trew tha front door, thass how we searled in.

My hart, thare wor a crowd. One or two on em down tha front even hed on them sharts mearde o' white cardboard, an they wor smookin segars. Them at tha back wor whisslin an golderin, an tha air wor as foisty as larst week's apple-pie.

* * *

Then tha lights come on over tha ring an a feller in black hopped in an stuck his hand up.

"Hare we go, Limpsy," I say.

"My lords, leardies an gennlemen," sharmed out this feller, "tha fust bout o' tha evenin will be Bout Number 2 on yar programme. I regret to announce thet tha contestants in Bout Number 1 hev so far fearled to appare. Booth wor present at tha weigh-in, but neither hev bin sin since."

"What did I tell yer?" I say as we jumped tew our feet, "Bob Rush ent hare."

"Mr. Chareman," sung out Fred Johnson. "I beg to differ with yar laarst remark. As mannidger o' tha comin warld champion, Jack (Limpsy)

Vardle, tha Demon o' Dumpton, I draw yar attenshun to tha fack thet my fighter is hare at tha ringside, ready an willin to box. Thass thet yeller Bob Rush o' Ticklin Saint Andrew whass missin. In them sarcumstances, my fighter clearm tha desishun an tha parse accordin to tha contrack."

I remember givin tree harty chares when Hitler lorst tha war, an another tree when them Japs give up, but I dornt know thet I fared to feel any more like charing then than what I did arter lissenin to Fred's speech. Arter all them weeks o' worry about Limpsy, thet hed all tarned out jest as we wanted. I set down in a sort o' dream – but then suffin fared to go wrong.

* * *

For a staart, thet struck me Fred wornt tha only one what hed bin hollerin. Then I see tha M.C. pearkin backwards an forrards from one side o' tha ring to tha other, fust at Fred an then at some other feller what stood oppersite. I haardly need tell yer my hart hit tha floor with a bang when this other feller sharmed out: "I'm Bob Rush. I hed thet on tha best orthority this chicken-livered shanny-brearn Vardle wornt comin tonight. I dornt believe he's hare, an I clearm tha parse as mine."

Thare wornt narthin for it. They lugged Limpsy orf to tha dressin-rume, an we went with him.

"What tha hike went wrong with Humpty?" say Fred.

"Thass tew learte to think about thet now," I say. "We'll jest hatta hope young Limpsy dornt git narthin warse than a few black eyes an a broken neck."

Me an tha boy Chaarlie acted as seckonds. We hed to hold Limpsey's knees apart as we got him inter tha ring, cos tha way they wor a-knockin, he might a done hisself a injery afore he staarted. We stood in his corner weartin for Bob Rush to come in, an a longer five minnits I never did know in all my born days.

In tha finnish Chaarlie say, Hare he come," he say, an if we hent a ketched hold o' tha ropes I'll lay we'd a fell down.

But thet wornt him at all. Thet wor tha M.C. He jumped inter tha ring and sharmed out: "My lords, leardies an gennlemen. Bob Rush of Ticklin Saint Andrew, hev bin forced to retire. Tha winner by default – Jack (Limpsy) Vardle, of Dumpton!"

* * *

As we went back to tha dressin-rume we run inter Humpty. He wor lookin marster pleased with hisself.

"What become o' Rush?" I say.

"Rush?" say Humpty. "For a staart his nearme ent Bob Rush at all, thass Bill Reed. Yew reckoned he left tha Army, dint yer? Well so he did dew – he wor a duzzy desarter. Thare's tew carnels, fower captins, an a sarjint-meajor weartin to give evidence agin him when they come out o' horspital. I found out a few things about Bob Rush afore I mearde a book on tha fight. Thass his bad luck thare charnced to be a couple o' milliterry policemen in his dressin-rume when he got thare."

An orf Humpty searled, jingling his pockets.

HARBERT
3rd May 1961

EIGHT OFFENDERS UP AT COURT

There wor a frorsty ow wind a-roarin up tha staircearse inter tha Flitmarsh Court when I tarned up to see tha Bench sort out them fellers what hed a dust-up over Gladys Cutch in tha darnce hall on tha Frida night.

Them ow wooden seats wor suffen cold, but they wor full o' wimmen with shoppin barskets an ow men what hed nipped in to git out o' tha wind cos thet wor wicked weather to stand thare proppin tha Poost Orfice up like they usually dew.

Thare wornt a single passon in tha Court what dint hev a scarf wropped round his neck or his collar tarned up, an tha way their breath come out like puffs o' steam thet put yew in mind of a rearlway stearshun.

* * *

Ow Lawyer Pinch set thare at his tearble, shiverin fit to fall to pieces, with his glarsses jumpin up an down on his greart red snout like a kettle boilin on a stove. His clark set alongside him, a-scribblin hard, either to mearke hisself look busy or else to keep warm.

Inspector Churkey wor stumpin up an down like a bull in a pen. Mr. Crawley o' Creep an Crawley, hed his hands round a fag-end, an tha only one what set thare imiteartin to look as if he never felt tha cold wor that greart long streak of a lawyer, Mr. Jellicoe Hickey, o' tha well-known firm o' Stott an Hickey.

"Silence!" hollered a policeman, but he needn't a bothered, cos thare wornt a deen in tha Court exceptin for pearple's teeth a-chatterin. An in from a door at tha back come Mr. Lucas Miffler, tha chareman o' tha Bench, follered by Miss Crimp, Buncombe, tha corn marchant, Elijah Frogg an Twinge tha union feller.

"Shut them winders!" say Mr. Miffler. "Oh, they are shut. Well then, shut them doors! Tha cold in hare is fit to..."

He dint say what thet wor fit for cos he ketched Miss Crimp's eye in time to stop hisself. "Tha heatin in this hare Court," he went on, "is a disgrearce to tha town. Thass up to tha Cownsil o see to it. Mearke a note on it, Mr. Clark."

Lawyer Pinch got harf out of his chare, nodded, and set down agin

* * *

"Now," say Mr. Miffler, "call tha offendants. An be quick about it, else we shall all freeze to dead."

Harf a dozen policemen hollered an in come Ted Gunn, Bob Freestone, Micka Parsons, Arthur Binks, an fower more what I din't reckernise. A chaarge o' brawlin, or scrappin, or causin an affray in a publick plearce, or however they put it, wor read out by Lawwyer Pinch at top speed, an they all pleaded not guilty.

Up got Mr. Jellicoe Hickey. "May thet please yar warships..." he say.

"Hold yew on, Mr. Stickey," say Mr. Miffler, "yew dornt hatta wearste tha time o' tha Court on a rarfty ow mornin tellin us who yew are. We all know yew. Yew're Mr. Stickey o' Hot an Stickey, an yew're for tha defense. I knew yar father well."

"Hickey, yar warships, Jellicoe Hickey, if yew will permit tha correckshun," say Mr. Hickey. "An I repersent one o' tha defendants in this cairse, Edward Gunn."

"Hickey or Sticky, what dew thet matters?" say Mr. Miffler, "This hare ent no weather to staart argifyin over trifles. We want to git at tha facks o tha cairse an git out o' hare afore tha blood freeze in our weins. Who did yew say yew repersented?"

"Gunn," say Mr. Hickey.

"What gun?" sharmed out Fresher Frogg, what hed bin readin some bits of ow newspearper what he fished out of his pocket, an consequently hent hud a ward o' what hed went on. "I dint know thare wor no gun mixed up in this hare. If thass a shootin affray we hent got tha power to deal with it, hev we, Mr. Chareman? We shall hatta send thet to tha Assizes, on't we?"

"Not gun, Gunn," say Mr. Miffler. "Gunn, Frogg, Gunn, not gun."

"Oh," say Fresher. "Well, thass diffrent. Only we want to be right about these hare things afore we staart. I mean to say, thare's cairses what we can try an cairses what we carnt try. Yew arst tha Clark, he'll bear me out."

* * *

Mr. Miffler give Fresher Frogg a look as much as to say he'd like to bear him out hisself, on a stretcher.

"Thare's one thing, bor," he say, " yew on't fall asleep today, not in this weather. Come yew on, now, Inspeckter, call tha evidence. Tha way tha time o' this hare Court is wearsted is a proper skandle."

"One moment, if thet please yar warships," cut in Mr. Crawley o' Creep an Crawley. "I appare for another o' tha defendants, Robert Freestone."

"Then why dint yew say so afore?" say Mr. !iffler. "We shall be all night afore we git to tha witnesses. What about tha rest on em, are they repersented?"

"Only Freestone an Gunn, yar warships," say Inspeckter Churkey.

"We shall hatta remember thet when tha time come," say Mr. Miffler. "Freestone repersented by Mr. Stickey, an Gunn repersented by Mr. Crawley. Alright, let's git on."

"Tha other way about, yar warships," say Mr. Hickey, drorin hisself up till he fared to look like a tellygrarf pole. "With respeck, may I clare up this matter once an for all. I appare for Gunn, an my larned frend hare appare for Freestone."

"Thass what I said," say Mr. Miffler. "Realy, if we keep on hevin all these hare innaruckshuns we sharnt never git hoom today. Call tha evidence! Hang on a minnit, thow. I shall want suffin to write with. Tha ink in this hare inkwell is friz over."

* * *

108

He prooged it with his pen-nib an then picked tha inkwell up an tarned thet upside-down.

"Thet must be thet thare stuff what tha wireless call 'black ice'," say Buncombe tha corn marchant, an larfed thet haard he looked like somebodda shearkin a sack o' tearters.

"Eh?" say Mr. Miffler, knockin tha bottom o' tha inkwell with tha handle of his pen.

"Narthin," say Buncombe.

"I thowt yew spook," say Mr. Miffler. "Thass time somebodda spook. Hare we are holdin up tha corse o' justice on account o' tha heatin being thet bad thare ent narthin but ice in tha chareman's inkwell. Thass another thing yew want to mearke a note on, Mr. Clark, when yew write to tha Cownsil. Dew yew smook, Inspeckter?"

"Not on dewty, yar warship," say Inspeckter Churkey.

"I dint arst if yew smooked on dewty. I arst if yew smooked," say Mr. Miffler. "Cos if yew dew, praps yew're got a lighter yew can lend me to thaw out this hare ink. Or if yew hent got a lighter, praps yew're got a match?"

In tha finish Lawyer Pinch conwinced Mr. Miffler to fotgit about tha inkwell an borrer his pen, but I shall hatta adjarn as them lawyers say, till next week.

HARBERT
18th January 1963

A PROPER OW MIX-UP – THASS ALL

Tha fust witness they called in tha cairse o' tha dust-up at tha darnce hall wor tha caretearker, ow Bart Freebody. They'd kept him weartin on tha stairs so long he wor dudderin with cold an coun't haardly keep hisself upright in tha witness-box.

"Whass got inter yew, Freebody?" arst Mr. Lucas Miffler, tha chareman o' tha Bench, arter pore ow Bart hed duzzy nare dropped tha Bible.

"Nothin what a drop o' rum woun't put right, yar warship," say ow Bart.

"Rum?" say Mr. Miffler. "Yew hent hed one tew many, hev yer?"

"No, thet I hent – I're hed fower or five tew few," say ow Bart.

"Well, yew on't git none till yew're finished yar evidence, so yew'd best git on with it an spit thet out right shaarp," say Mr. Miffler. "We could all dew with a drop o' rum on a morning like this hare – leastways, I dornt know about Miss Crimp – praps yew prefar a nip o' gin, dew yer, Miss Crimp? – thass what tha leardies like as a rule. Howsomever, hare we shall hatta set with our snouts droppin orf till justice a bin done. So stop wearstin tha Court's time and say what yew're gotta say."

* * *

Miss Crimp shot a look full o' pins an needles at Mr. Miffler, bein tha sort o' woman what spend har time collectin prayer-books to send to savidges, an writin to tha pearpers about tha evils o' drink. Yew woun't git gin parst har lips without yew used one o' them things tha vet give a hoss pills with.

"Now then, Freebody," say Inspeckter Churkey. "What did yew see on tha night o' tha darnce?"

"I see a feller pick up a drum an fetch another feller a sisserara alongside tha skull with it," say ow Bart.

"Darnce, what darnce?" say Mr. Miffler. "We hent hud no evidence about no darnce."

"Yew must a bin dreamin, Mr. Miffler," say Miss Crimp, right pleased with harself for gittin har own back. "Tha Inspeckter explearned all about tha darnce in his openin remarks. I really carnt see no need for tha Bench to hatta set hare in this weather an lissen to it twice over."

"Thass what I keep on tellin em," say Mr. Miffler. "Tha way tha police persent their evidence is shockin. Either they give us narthin at all to go on or they give us tha searme thing twice over. Yew hud what Miss Crimp sed, Inspeckter. We dornt want tha evidence twice over. Without yew git a muve on we shall be hare all night."

* * *

Inspeckter Churkey carst his glimmers up at tha ceilin as if he wor beggin it to fall on Mr. Miffler's hid, an put him out of his misery.

"Can yew identify tha fellers in Court?" he arst Bart Freebody.

"What them in tha dock?" say ow Bart. "Well him on tha end thare is Ted Gunn, what play tha drums in tha band. Tha one next to him is Bob Freestone, an then come…"

"No, I mean can yew tell tha Bench which one hit who with tha drum?" say tha Inspeckter.

"Not for sartain," say ow Bart. "My eyesight ent what thet used to be. But they wor all in it together."

Twinge, the union feller, what allers speak up when he set on tha Bench, jest to show he tearke his posishun sarious, butted in. "What wor yew dewin at tha darnce, Mr. Freebody?" he say.

"I wor thare in my offishal cappassity," say ow Bart. "I're gotta clare up arter them young uns, an without I'm behind em all tha time they leave bottles an fag-packets all over tha shop. Tearke thet thare darnce – thass a wonder they could darnce at all, tha amount o' muck an rubbish layin about. Tha trouble with young pearple today is they dornt git proper correckshun at hoom. If their fathers an mothers…"

"Quite right," say Mr. Miffler. "Yew want to lissen to what he say, yew lot in tha dock. Yew wouldn't be in tha dock at all if yew'd paid a bit more attenshun to what yar fathers an mothers telled yer when yew wor little. Hullin ow rubbish about in tha street, thass disgrearceful."

* * *

"May thet please yar warships," sung out Mr. Crawley, of Creep an Crawley, an Mr. Jellicoe Hickey, of Stott an Hickey.

"Arter yew, Mr. Crawley," say Mr. Hickey.

"Arter yew, Mr Hickey," say Mr. Crawley.

"Now what is it?" arst Mr. Miffler. "Time's goin on an my feet are numb. I carnt put up with many more o' these hare innerruckshuns."

"May I remind yar warship," say Mr. Hickey, "thet neither my client nor any o' tha defendants is hare on a chaarge o' depositin litter in tha highway. Thet'd help tha Court if tha evidence wor kept strickly rellevant."

"Thank yew, Mr. Stickey, thass jest what I're bin sayin all along," say Mr. Miffler. "Keep it revelant, an praps we shall git hoom some time tonight. Let me arst yew a question, Freebody. Did yew or did yew not see these hare young uns lammin inter one another an kickin up a hallabaloo?"

"Thass right," say ow Bart.

"Alright, then," say Mr. Miffler. "Next witness. Unless yew want to say suffin else, Mr Stickey?"

"Hickey, yar warship," say Mr Hickey, raisin tew his full height till he could a sin over tha top of a bus. "An I sartainly dew want to say suffin else. Now Mr. Freebody, are yew prepared to sware – think careful, mind, an remember yew're on oath – are yew prepared to sware yew saw Edward Gunn offer wiolence to anyone whatsoever?"

"I carn't sware to who done what," say ow Bart. "Thet wor a proper ow mix up, thass all I know."

"A pro-per ow m-i-x-u-p," say Mr. Miffler, a-writin on it down. "Consarn it, Mr. Clark, this hare pen yew lent me a run out o' juice. I shall hatta git tha ice orf o' this hare inkwell after all. Give us yar lighter, Buncombe.

* * *

Buncombe parssed Mr. Miffler his lighter, an Mr. Miffler held tha inkwell up with one hand time he barned tha lighter under it with tha other. Fresher Frogg bent over an pearked inter tha inkwell like a cook seein how tha soup wor gittin on.

I dornt know exackly how thet happened – if tha fire cracked tha inkwell or what – but all of a sudden thare wor a splutter an Fresher Frogg's fearce went as black as midnight. Yew should a hud tha larfter in Court as he set thare with ink drippin orf his mustash.

I reckoned thet wor time I went. I hud a policeman hollerin "Silence!" as I nipped down tha stairs. Arterwards they telled me tha cairse larsted another hour, an them fellers wor bound over.

HARBERT
25th January, 1963

FRED'S CAR IN A DIFFRENT CLARSS

Ow Dan Forster reckon this hare weather thet we're bin hevin ent not narthin. "I remember one time," he say, "tha snow wor thet deep tha angels wor playin snowballs."

"Thet friz that haard tha tea went solid comin out o' tha spout, an yew hed to breark thet orf an eat thet like sticks o' barley-sugar."

I carnt help what ow Dan say, thass bin mucky ow weather as far as what I'm consarned. But yew dornt want to hare about tha marster's totty little ow pump a-freezin up, an him not hevin no water, an his missis imiteartin to git tha gal Alice to run backards an forrards with buckets an them hevin a duzzy row what nigh on got me tha sack, an all tha snow-shovellin what I're bin dewin round tha yaard till my back fare as if thass brook.

*   *   *

Corse, thass alright for tha marster. He spend more on whiskey than what 1 arn. He can keep warm. Mind yew, thass another thing – us runnin short o' coal an tha coal marchant not bein earble to git his caart up tha drift. Tha marster put young Wicks on to choppin up tha tree what fell in thet thare gearle larst summer, an then tha marster's missis telled tha gal Alice she could hev some o' tha wood if she fetched thct from whare Wicks wor a-choppin on it, only she'd got to fetch enough to fill tha marster's shud fust.

Thare wor another duzzy row then I'm tellin yer. Tha gal Alice reckon she ent no sarvant o' tha marter's missis, even if 1 dew wark for him. Howsomever, like I say, yew dornt want to hare narthin about thet thare, so I'd best tell yer about Fred Johnson's new car.

Well, thet ent a new car, not what yew'd call new. Thaas a 1949 model. I forgit what he reckon thet is – a Frawde V-8 Collapsible, I think he say.

Yew know Fred, he allers did charge about on a motor-bike, an since he're got a wife an family thass bin cars what he go arter. I dornt know how many he hent hed in tha parst six or seven yare.

Tha larst one he hed wor a proper junk-yaard speshal, an this hare ent a lot better.

"I'm pickin on it up this marnin," he say to me tha other day.

"Dew that go?" I arst

"Go?" he say. "Lor, bor. like a duzzy bomb."

"Yew mean thet blow to pieces?" I arst.

"Dornt talk squit," he say. "When a car's in fust clarss runnin order, us motorists say thet go like a bomb. Thass an expreshun what we use."

"Oh," I say. "Only tha larst harf duzzen cars what yew're hed all blew to bits, so I wondered."

"For tha yare," say Fred, "by which I mean for its earge, this hare car is what they call immackerlate. An thare ent a lot o' muck on it neither. Theet a bin chofer driven an meartearned by one metriculous owner since new. Thet a only done 110,000 miles – an for one o' them Frawde V-8 Collapsible enjines thet ent not narthin."

* * *

"Did yew say chofer driven?" I arst.

"Thass right," say Fred.

"Who wor tha chofer?" I arst.

"Well, he wornt exackly a chofer," say Fred. "Smatter o' fack thet wor Harold Hagg at Flitmarsh – he bowt thet in a ockshun an he're used thet ever since as a taxi."

"I know it," I say. "I're sin it." I dint tell him whare I see it. Thet wor runnin bakards down tha Beacon Hill one arternune with steam comin out o' tha front end an tha brearkes brook.

"Tha thing about a big car," say Fred, "is yew git thet for less than what yew hatta pay for a little un. An think what yew git for tha money. I carnt think o' narthin thet thare car hent got ceptin a billiard tearble."

"I mean to say, tha seats are real leather for a staart. Then thet a got a wireless set in it, an a heater, an a fog lamp, and a thing to stick a bunch o' flowers in, Thare's enough rume inside for my wife an kids and my father an mother as well.

"Thass whare I mearde my mistearke afore – buyin totty little ow cars what give my missis tha cramp in tha back thare with har knees up. when for less money I could a got suffin in a diffrent clarss altogether. Corse, thet eat up a bit more petrol, an thet corst more to insure, but I reckon thass warth it."

Thet'd be about harf arter tew in tha arternune when I see Fred an tha boy Chaarlie a-sarnterin up tha Diddlin rood with a scuppet apiece.

"Come yew on, boy Harbert," sung out Chaarlie, "yew can give us a hand to crowd thet back on to tha rood."

* * *

I hent got a lot o' book-larnin, but I can put tew an tew together like lightnin. What with them scuppets for shovellin tha snow, an him arstin me to give em a hand crowdin suffin back on to tha rood, thet dint tearke me a seckond to wark out thet thet wor Fred's car they wor a-talkin about.

114

"What a yew hed a acksident, boy Fred?" I arst.

"Thet ent not narthin," say Fred.

"One o' tha tires hed got tew much wind in it, an bumpin an skitherin over tha ice along tha rood, thet bust. I skidded bang inter a grup, so thare she lay now, snout down in a snow-drift, an back wheels up in tha air."

I went along with em, an my hart yew coun't see much o' Fred's car. Thet wor daark afore we got thet dug out, an in tha finish they hed to git a trackter tew it.

He hent hed thet out agin since, but he reckon when tha warm weather come thet'll go like a bomb.

* * *

P.S. I writ this hare afore tha frorst fared to give a bit. Now I'm a-stickin on it in tha poost thass begun to thow an thare's all sluss. Let's hope by tha time yew read it tha snow's all gorn away.

HARBERT
1st February, 1963

LUMPS O' PLARSTER ON MY CHEST

Thass one thing about not hevin no piped water, yew hent got no pipes to bust, hev yer? I reckon we're bin better orf at Dumpton than all them other willages what a hed tha pipes laid on.

Howsomever, I hent got time to write much this week cos all my ceilins are down.

My hart. thares a rum ow mess in my upstares. Thet ent tha pipes, like I say, cos we hent got none, but our ow rufe hent hed no attenshun for I dornt know how long, an them ow tiles coun't stand up to narthin once tha snow staarted to thow, and down harf a duzzen on em come, an all tha water poured in on top o' tha bedrume ceilins, an afore we knew it thare wor plarster all over everywhare.

* * *

115

I laid thare in bed in tha middle o' tha night dreamin I wor in one o' them wrestlin matches agin a feller tha size of a charch steeple, an all of a sudden he come down swop on top o' my chest, an I hud tha referee hollerin, "Git yew up! Git yew up, Harbert! Git yew up!"

Only thet wornt tha ref at all, thet wor tha gal Alice, an thet wornt this feller on my chest, thet wor a duzzy greart lump o' plarster.

"Git yew out on it, Harbert," say tha gal Alice, "tha ceilin's comin down."

"Whare? What ceilin?" I say.

"Why, our ceilin, yew fewl yew,"she say. "Wearke yew up, dew. Hang on a minnit time I light tha light. Waaahhggghh! Thare go another lump!"

Tha ow brarss bed-poost went "Donngg!" as enough plarster to mearke a grearve-stoon ketched thet on tha way down. Then tha gal Alice lit tha light an tha inside o' tha bedrume fared to look like a flour-mill. Thare wor white dust thick in tha air what yew could tearste on yar tongue an booth on us staarted to sneeze.

"Tha twins!" sung out tha gal Alice. "If tha ceilin's down in their rume thet'll kill em!"

* * *

We booth sprung out o' bed at once an got jammed in tha door. Howsomever, I got inter tha little ow rume whare tha twins sleep afore the gal Alice, an fished em out o' their little ow beds for har to see to.

I wor jest in time an all, cos as I stood thare imiteartin to see if tha ceilin wor a-goin to give, thare wor a drip-drip-drip o' water, an then a proper rush, an down come harf tha plarster on my skull.

We put tha twins to sleep on tha sofa in tha front rume, well wropped up, cos we hent hed no fire in thare, an then I got as much as what I could o' our bed things out o' our bedrume an we slept in tha kitchen. Leastways, we dint sleep cos we wore a-chunterin all night long about them ceilins an what I'd hatta say to tha marster tha nexter mornin.

I'll say this hare for tha marster, he come an give one look an then sent me to tha bilders to tell him to come an mend tha rufe an tha ceilins urgent.

* * *

On tha way hoom agin I nipped round to my Ma's in tha loke to see how she wor gittin on. Pore ow thing, she dornt git no younger, but she's full o' go. Har ceilin wor down in har front bedrume as well.

"I dornt know what I'm a-goin to dew, boy Harbert," she say, "an thass a fack. I carnt afford to hev thet done up, not out o' my penshun. I reckon I'll hatta dew tha best I can."

"I'll see tew it," I say. "I'll git Fred Johnson in, he'll dew it as a fearvour, an me an him can git thet done betwixt us."

"Yew'll hatta pay him," say my Ma. "He on't dew it for narthin. He got a family to keep, tha searme as what yew hev. An thet ent right yew should spend yar money what yew carnt afford, not on yar wearges yew carnt."

"I'll see thet git done," I say.

They're tha ones I fared to feel right-down sorry for, all them old uns like my Ma what hed screarped an searved an owned their own cottidges an dint hev narthin to mend em with but their penshuns. I mean to say, thass alright for me, my cottidge belong to tha marster, an thass his job to put thet right.

Then thare's all them what live in housin what belong to Ow Mother Quail, har up at tha Hall. A fat lot she're done to keep them cottidges in order all these yares.

* * *

When I got hold o' Fred Johnson to see about my Ma's ceilin, he reckoned his wor as bad if not warse, an his house belong to Mrs. Quail.

" Yew know how long I're bin at har to dew suffin about my chimney," he say. "But she on't lift a finger. Now she'll hatta dew suffin, cos all our top floor is like a duck-pond with lumps o' plarster swimmin in it.

"An I ent tha only one. I reckon harf har properties a got their ceilins down. Thet'll corst har a pretty penny. Only I reckon we shall all hatta maarch up to tha Hall with banners an a big drum afore she git tha bilders in."

I charnced to run inter Billy More-or-Less Hooper, so I tipped him tha wink. Arter all, he's our repersentative on tha Beethoe an Bedstead Rewral Districk Cownsil an if he carnt git narthin done nobodda can.

"Tha way I more or less look at it," say ow Billy, drorin hisself up an stickin his thumbs in his weskit pockets, "this hare come under tha headin o' publick health. Now yew know more or less as well as what I dew, all tha yares what I're more or less bin a member o' tha Cownsill. I're bin what I might call fightin for tha rights o' tha tennents.

"A ceilin is a ceilin an a rufe is a rufe," say ow Billy, "an they more or less come under diffrent seckshuns o' tha Act. A ceilin is more or less inside tha strucksher, an by wirtue o' what I might call tha agreement thet may or may not be tha responsibilita o' tha owner. On tha other hand , speakin by an large, a rufe is more or less on tha outside o' tha strucksher an if thass what I call a fault in tha rufe what dammidge tha ceilin then thass tha owner's clare responsibilita.

"So if tha owner more or less refuse, incline, delay or otherwise prognosticearte in tha performance of his dewty to git tha rufe sin to, all I're gotta dew is rearse thet at tha next Cownsil meetin as a more or less urgent matter o' publick health of what I might refar to as greart publick importance. Let me know how yew git on. Good mornin."

An thare thet lay. All I can say is, publick health or no publick health, a lot o' wimmen a got a lot o' haard wark ahid on em with pans an brushes.

HARBERT
15th February, 1963

THET'S DONE HUMPTY NO HAARM

Thare ent but one feller in Dumpton what a done well out a' tha cold weather, an thass Humpty Potter. He're bin sellin bottles o' brandy for medisinal parposes left, right an senter. He reckon he got em when they wor sellin up a hotel, but I know he dint.

Still thare, that ent for us to grumble when he let us hev em for harf price. An thet must be legal else tha policeman woun't a hed one orf of him.

Mind yew, like tha rest on us, Humpty ent bin earble to git about a lot. Moost o' tha time yew'd find him settin in his shud borin holes in chests o' drawers to look like tha wood-warm, so he can sell em as genuiwine anteeks.

* * *

His one good bit o' bisness wor when he found a werra ow book in one o' them chests o' drawers. Thet wor a sort of a prayer-book, with an ow leather cover, an brown spots on all tha pearges, an a lot o' thet funny ow print inside, all nobs an spikes.

I fust hud about it from tha Wicar. Thet fare as if Humpty went to tha Wicar's one night an say, "Reverend," he say, "I never did hev tha charnce to be a skolard, an I hent got much book-larnin. I can write a letter when I're got to, but thet ent tha sort o' letter what I'd want a real skolard to read. Yew're a larned man, an a gennleman, an I wor wonderin if yew'd dew me tha fearvour o' writin me a letter in proper gennleman's langwidge, if I tell yew what to put."

"Sartainly, Mr Potter," say tha Wicar, thinklin to hisself thet tha biggest rarscals on arth are humble men when thet come to tha point.

"I'm werra much obliged to yer," say Humpty. "Cos this hare letter I're gotta write is above my clarss. I dornt want to mearke a fewl of myself."

"Thass hartenin to hare yew say so," say tha Wicar. "Many a man in yar posishun woun't hev tha curridge to admit it. Now what dew yew want me to put?"

"Well now, Reverend," say Humpty. "Yew can staart orf. 'Dare Sar,' Then say suffin like, 'They reckon yew're got one harf o' tha Chelchester Missile.' "

"Tha Chelchester what?" arst tha Wicar.

"Missile," say Humpty. "Leastways thass what a expart reckoned that wor called."

* * *

"Missile?" say tha Wicar. "Chelchester Missile?" An then his ow glimmers lit up an his hart begun to beat like a steam-enjin. "Yew dornt mean tha Chelchester Missal, Dew yew? Is this hare some sort o' ow book what yew're talkin about?"

"Thass right," say Humpty. "Thass a sort of a prayer-book. 'Tha Chelchester Missile' they call it. Yew hetta forgive me if I dornt say it proper. Like I told yer, I ent no skolard. Howsomever, what I want to say is: 'Dare Sar, They reckon yew're got one harf o' tha Chelchester Missile an woun't mind gittin yar hands on tha other harf. If thass right, yar charnce a come, cos by acksident I happen to a got it in my colleckshun.

Thass a big disappointment to me to hatta brearke up my colleckshun, but things bein what they are on tha Stock Exchearnge an one thing an another, I're come to tha conclusion tha best thing I can dew is let yew hev my harf at a fair price, cos I on't never hev enough money to buy yar harf, an thet'd be a shearme if arter all these hare yares tha ow book wornt all in one lump. Yars sinsarely…' An then I'll sign it."

"Bless my soul," say tha Wicar. "I carnt say I know a greart lot about bibberlologery*, but I dew seem to a hud o' tha Chelchester Missal. Am I to understand yew are in posseshun o' one harf, an want to sell it to somebodda what possess tha other harf?"

"Thass about tha long an tha short on it," say Humpty.

"Wharever did yew git it?" arst tha Wicar, givin Humpty a funny ow look.

"I picked thet up for a song with a lot of ow rubbish when they wor sellin up an ow hall in Rutland." say Humpty. "I never knew I'd got it till I got hoom an sorted tha stuff out. An then I dint know what thet wor till I took thet to a big expart on these hare matters. Yew may know him. He's Canon Upwright – him thet come an wisit tha Rewral Dean."

"Bless my soul. Canon Upwright. Yes, indeed, a greart man, a greart man," say tha Wicar. "Well, I carnt say I approve o' yar references to bein a collector with inwestments on tha Stock Exchearnge, but if yew'll parmit me to tone thet down a bit, I'll write yew tha letter. Now sposin we put thet like this hare…"

An tha Wicar writ a marster dignified sort o' letter for Humpty to sign.

Like I told yew, thet wor on account o' tha Wicar gettin excited about this hare discovery o' Humpty's thet I come to hare about it in tha fust plearce. But since then I're found out a few things what tha Wicar dornt know.

* * *

To staart with, thet wor right enough about Humpty findin thet thare prayer-book in a load o' junk, cos they wor in one o' them ow drawers. But what he dint tell tha Wicar wor thet he found tha hull book, not jest a harf on it.

Another thing he dint tell tha Wicar wor thet he'd come acrorst them sort o' books afore, an he knew this one worn't warth more 'n ten quid. I mean to say, he know them collectors, and he know tha walue o' tha things they collect better'n what they dew.

120

Likewise he know when a collector a got suffin another collector want, tha price go up. So he tore thet thare book in harf, run orf to tha sorftest collector in tha county, an got his ten quid for one harf on it.

Thass when he nipped round to tha Wicar an got him to write tha letter. I dornt know what nearme he signed thet with, but one thing is sartain, thet worn't his own. Thet must a bin suffin more like 'Marmaduke Uffington-Buggley', and I reckon he sent thet from some address of some crook he know a long way away.

* * *

All I know is, thet thare collector what bowt tha fust harf orf of him is tha kind o' feller what'd set up all night dreamin o' findin tha other harf in a second-hand shop somewhare. An when he got this hare letter from Uffington-Buggley, or whatever Humpty signed hisself, he'd be up tha wall an round tha bend till he'd bowt tha other harf o' tha book so as he could brag about it to his frends.

Thass no good yew arstin me how much Humpty stung him for in tha finish. All I know is, Humpty a bin settin at hoom all trew tha bad weather watchin tha price go up. If he dint mearke tha best paart of a hunderd quid on tha deal I'd be surprised.

He wor in tha Fox tha other night when Fred Johnson charnced to say, "Harf a loaf is better'n no bread."

"Sometimes thass better'n a hull loaf," said Humpty.

HARBERT
22nd February, 1963

Harbert seems to have made a brave attempt at "bibliography" – Editor

NEWS FROM DUMPTON
by Harbert

THET RICH CUZZEN'S NEVER COME!

What I keep arstin myself is what I'd a done if I'd a bin Enoch Fletcher. I mean if I'd a bin enjoyin a quiet drink in tha Fox an then all of a sudden Billy More-or-Less Hooper hed shown me a letter sayin my long-lorst cuzzen, what hed mearde a forechune in Texas, wor on his way to Dumpton to see me.

I reckon I'd a done what Enoch done. I'd a let out a holler like what yew'll hare at Carrer Road if tha City beat Lester , an then I'd a gorn dead white, set down in a chare, an spent the next five minnits swallerin brandy to steady my narves.

"Lor, bor," say Fred Johnson, "yew can kiss them ow pigs o' yars goodbye. Yew'll be rich! Yew on't want pigs, yew'll be keepin rearce-hosses."

* * *

"Thass if this hare cuzzen o' his tearke a fancy to him," say tha boy Chaarlie. "Thet ent everabodda what could tearke a fancy to Enoch."

"Hold yew yar duller, bor," say Billy Hooper. "Enoch is more or less as good a frend as what any sittizen o' these hare parts a ever hed. I more or less speak as I find, and while I'm bound to more or less admit thet over tha yares, by an laarge, we've hed our ups an downs, him an me, I'll say this for him – in times o' good forchune he're never bin one to grudge his meartes a pint.

"If I know him as well as what I more or less think I know him, he'll be out o' thet thare chare in a minnit arskin Tom Drew hare to sarve drinks all round."

Enoch give ow Billy a look, but he dint argew. By this time his cheeks wor back to their normal culler, sort o' harfway betwixt a raddish an a beetrute, an his glimmers wor shinin like glow-warms.

"Open up a bottle o' best Scotch whisky Tom!" he sung out. "This hare call for a celebrearshun! My hart alive, who'd a thowt a son of ow One-Eyed Fletcher'd ever come back to Dumpton! Arter all these yares, an him warth millions! Git yew a shift on, Tom, let's be havin them drinks!"

* * *

I dornt want to accuse Tom Drew o' bein money-minded, but thet wornt ten seckonds afore he wor whisperin suffin to his eldest boy trew tha door at tha back o' tha bar. An thet wornt another ten seckonds afore tha boy flashed parst tha winder with his cap an wropper on, an arter thet tha way tha Fox filled up wor a maarvel.

Enoch reckoned arterwards he wor proper flattered at tha number o' frends what dropped in to drink to his good forchune, an as far as what I could mearke out, the sum agin Enoch's nearme on tha slearte stood at eight quid odd by closin-time.

We wor all well warmed up when Billy More-or-Less Hooper slapped his hand on tha counter an hollered for quiet.

"Colleegs an gennlemen," he say, "I dornt want to innerupt what I might call tha jollificearshuns, but like I allers say, bisness more or less come afore pleasure, an we hent settled tha bisness o' tha meetin yit.

"As some on yar know, an as others may or may not know, this hare gatherin consarn a letter more or less addressed to tha Mayor o' Dumpton – thass as much as to say, by an laarge, an with due respeck to them what think otherwise, addressed to me.

"In this hare letter Enoch's American cuzzen, whass more or less in Manchester at this present time, arst me to find him lodgins in Dumpton. Now I more or less put thet to the meetin – whare else should I find him lodgins but along o' Enoch? I say thare ent no question o' him stayin any plearce else. All in fearvour more or less siggernify in tha usual manner."

* * *

We all siggernified in tha moost unusual manner o' hollerin at tha tops o' our woices "Good ow Enoch!" an "Up tha Green Faarm!" But Enoch stuck his glarss down, pulled his snout, an fared to look a bit flummoxed about suffin.

"Hello," say Tom Drew, "Whass up with yew, Enoch?"

"I dornt know," say Enoch. "Thass one thing to find out yew're got a rich cuzzen whass on his way to see yer. Thass another to think o' what sort o' bed yew're a-goin to give him to sleep in. I're hed a run o' bad luck this larst several yare. My ow farnicher ent what a rich man's used to."

An thass when suffin happened what mearde me think tha wor suffin funny about this hare bisness. Humpty Potter spook.

* * *

Humpty hed bin settin thare all tha evenin keepin hisself to hisself. He hent haardly opened his gob, except to hull his whisky in it, an thet ent like him.

"Yew dornt want to disgrearce yarself, Enoch," he say. "Yew want to mearke a good impreshun. A wealthy feller like him – if he's lookin for suffin to dew with his money, yew want to put him in a good frearme o' mind. He'll hatta hev a nice sorft bed and a bit o' desent farnicher about him."

"I dornt know whare I'm a-goin to git it," say Enoch. "Not by Wensda. I carnt buy new stuff, an if I could they woun't deliver it in tha time. An thare ent no orkshuns tomorrer thet I know on."

* * *

Humpty looked round tha company to see they wornt a-lissenin – which they wornt, cos they wor all larfin and talkin among theirselves agin. Then he give Enoch harf a wink an wagged his hid as much as to say, "Come yew a bit closer."

"I dornt want to stick my snout in whare thet ent wanted," he say. "But if thass a question o' gittin suffin done in a hurry I reckon I can help yer. Thass jest by good luck I charnce to hev some rare nice farnicher what I got tha other day for a speshal customer when they sold up an ow hall in Suffolk. As a fearvour to yew, as a frend, I could let yew hev a bit on it, an my other customer can weart."

Enoch's fearce lit up. "What a yew got, bor?" he arst.

They must a set thare talking about farnicher, an prices, an I dornt know what else, for the next harf an hour. I dint hare all on it, but I remember Humpty sayin thet'd be a sacrifice on his paart to tearke ten quid for a genuwine anteek bed mearde o' walnut, an another twenty quid for tha dressin-tearble, warsh-stand an wardrobe to match. An thare wornt no sense hevin a posh new bedrume sweet without carpets an cartains to go with it, an a chare or tew.

* * *

Tha nexter mornin I see Humpty's hoss-an-caart tarn inter Enoch's piled high. On tha Wensda Enoch wor sarnterin about in his pepper-an-salt weskit an billycock hat smookin a segar, weartin for his rich cuzzen to tarn up.

124

But tha thing is he never did tarn up. We hent sin hair or hide on him from thet day to this. Billy More-or-Less Hooper reckon he's bound to come any day now, cos thare's tha letter to pruve it, an yew carnt git round suffin whass down in black an white. Enoch say he think his cuzzen must a got called away on argent bisness.

Me, I ent sayin one thing nor yit tha other. But when I think o' tha pile o' money Humpty took orf o' Enoch for them few sticks o' farnicher, I staart wonderin. I mean, thet thare letter come from Manchester , dint it? Well. Humpty went to Manchester on tha saturda to see tha Canearies beat Manchester City in tha Cup.

HARBERT
29th March, 1963

SIDE THA SEA WI' THA GAL GLADYS

Corse, I can unnerstand why young fellers run arter Gladys Cutch. She's tha best-lookin mawther for miles round, and tha way she souse harself in stuff out of a bottle she smell like a bucket o' sweet peas.

But tha way she muck tha boys about, thass a wonder they dornt form a union an put har on tha black list.

Tearke young John Diddley, what live at Corlin All Saints. He oughter know better. Yit what dew he dew but arst har if she'd like to go to Yarmouth with him on tha back o' his motor-bike. And when she reckoned thet'd be luvly, he wor thet pleased with hisself he went an paid for four rounds o' drinks in tha Green Man afore he knew what he wor a-dewin.

Silly young fewl, he's thet keen on tha gal Gladys his hid's full o' charch bells. He might a known he wor lettin hisself in for suffin when she arst him if he wor fond o' kids. But he's thet far gorn, all he could think of wor him an har out for a jam round with a pram. Thet sounded to him like she wor thinkin about marridge, searme as hisself, so he telled

125

har yes, he wor suffin fond o' kids, an fixed up to meet har with his motor-bike on tha Saturda.

* * *

Well, they got to Yarmouth, an thare wor some crowd o' pearple along tha front an on tha beach, and she telled him to pull up outside some hotel or other. No suner wor they pulled up than along come a woman with a boy about eleven on one hand an another about nine on tha other.

"Yew found us alright, then, Annie," sung out tha gal Gladys. "Boy John, this is my cuzzen Annie an ha little ow young uns, Jimma and Fredda. This hare's tha boy John Diddley what wor kind enough to give me a lift."

"Pleased to meet yer," say this hare Annie.

"How are yer?" say tha boy John.

"Give us an ice-cream, Mister," say young Jimma.

"I'll slosh yew in a minnit," say Annie. "How many times dew I hatta tell yer –consarn it, boy Fredda, git yar hands orf o' tha gennleman's motor-bikc!"

"He en't dew no haarm," say tha boy John, fangin hold o' young Fredda's hand jest afore harf his enjine got pulled to bits. "Now then, be a good boy, Fredda – hey, hold on, young Jimma, thet thare's tha carberetter, yew'll muck thct up if yew ent careful! My hart, missis, yew're got a cupple o' lively young uns hare, thet yew hev."

"He like kids," say tha gal Gladys.

"Thass alright, then," say Annie. "What are we a-goin to dew?"

"I reckon tha fust thing is for tha boy John to find somewhare to stick his bike," say tha gal Gladys, "an then I should think tha kids'd like to go to tha sarcus."

"Cor!" shruck them kids. "Are we a-goin to tha sarcus? I want to see tha clowns! I want to see tha ellafants!"

"Yew on't see narthin if yew dornt hold still," say Annie. "Yew'll find rume for yar bike on tha other side o' tha rood thare, Mr. Diddley. We'll weart hare for yer."

* * *

As young John Diddley mooched about lookin for somewhare to leave his bike, he wornt feelin up to a sight. I mean to say, he staarted out thinkin he wor sposed to be hevin a day at the seaside along o' tha gal

Gladys. Har cuzzen Annie an a pair o' young uns wor suffin he hent bargined for.

Howsomever, he'd chared hisself up a bit by tha time he got em tha sarcus an wor dippin his hand in his pocket to git tha tickets. He wor jest a-goin to sing out, "Three an tew harves," when he got another shock: He could a swore he hud tha gal Gladys say "Ta-ta, boy John – hev a good time."

"Paarden?" he say.

"What a yew deaf or suffin?" arst tha gal Gladys. "Me an Annie wor jest sayin cheerio till we see yew agin arter tha sarcus."

"Wh-whadda yew mean – ch-cheerio – I mean to say – consarn it, ent yew comin inter tha sarcus as well?"

"Whatever give yew thet idea?" say tha gal Gladys. "I arst yew, Annie, ent men tha limit? What'd we want to go to tha sarcus for? I carnt stick sarcuses."

"Nor yit carnt I," say Annie. "But thet wor kind on yer to orfer to tearke tha kids I'm sure they'll enjoy it."

By this time tha feller in tha ticket-orfice wor kickin up a row about young John holdin' up tha queue, an afore he knew what wor happenin he'd got tha tickets in his hand an wor swep inside tha sarcus with tha rest o' tha crowd.

* * *

By what he telled us arterwards. tha rest o' tha day wor a duzzy nightmare. He wor fewl enough to git them kids some monkey-nuts, an they staarted hullin em all over tha shop. Twice he wor warned if he dint keep his kids in order he'd be hulled out.

He got em an ice-cream to keep em quiet, an a feller in a straw hat what got harf an ice-cream down tha back of his neck hed to be held down to discurridge him from wipin young John one alongside tha snout.

A fat woman in tha row behind kept sayin thet wor disgrearceful tha way fathers browt their kids up nowadays. She reckoned if John wor har husband she'd drownd harself. Tha boy John telled har thet if he wor har husband he woun't stop her, an she imitearted to fetch him one on tha skull with har handbag.

Thet wor bad enough in tha sarcus, but thet wor warse still when they got out agin, cos he coun't see tha gal Gladys an' har cuzzen Annie nowhare, an he dint know which way they'd gorn.

He wor up a lamp-poost imiteartin to get young Fredda down when Jimma hulled a bucket o' sea-water over some woman what lay on tha beach, an then a policeman tarned up an demarnded to know what wor goin on.

All he got out o' tha gal Gladys in tha finish wor: "If yew hent a said yew wor fond o' kids I woun't never a browt yer. An arter tha shearmeful way yew're trearted my cuzzen Annie's little daarlins yew can think yarself lucky if I ever speak to yer agin."

Tha boy John reckon next time he see tha gal Gladys comin he'll tarn an run.

HARBERT
31st July, 1964

PORE OW ELI – PROPER PITTIFUL

Arter ow Bob Blewitt went, thet left ow Dan Forster as tha oldest inhabitant. Thass if yew dornt count ow Eli Wicks, an yew carnt count him, cos by rights his cottidge is in Diddlin.

I dornt know for sartain how old ow Dan is, but he's several yare short o' ow Eli. Any time yew go up tha Diddlin rood yew can see ow Eli pokin about with his stick an mutterin tew hisself. Thass a pittiful thing to git old.

Corse, all tha Wicks family down tha Fen Cottidges, they're sort o' nephews an neeces o' his, but he never did want much to dew with em. He will live in thet thare ow cottidge on his own, thet dornt matters what they say.

I see him tha other night as I come down tha Diddlin rood on my bike, an I took thet inter my hid to cut him a cabbidge an tearke thet tew him.

So up I went along o' ow Mrs. Wicks what wor on har way to go an scrub his floor for him, like she dew.

* * *

Tha ow feller set thare alongside his tearble, what wor all swidges o' tea what he'd spilt, with a loof o' bread layin in one on em an milk-bottles

128

all over tha shop. He wor eatin bread-an-jam as best as what he could.

"I're browt somebodda to see yer, Grandad," say ow Mrs. Wicks. Corse, he ent har Grandad rearly, but thass what she call him.

The minnit he hud our woices, ow Eli fussicked about on tha tearble till he found his tea-caddy, an shut tha lid down snap.

"Yew dornt want to worry about yar tea, Grandad," say Mrs. Wicks. "Harbert on't nick it."

"They come when I'm abed an they nick it," say ow Eli.

Mrs Wicks pawked about in a corner an found a bucket. Then she blew a bit o' life inter tha fire an put tha kettle on.

"How are yew a-goin on, Eli?" I arst.

"I'm a-dewin, I'm a-dewin," say Eli. "Sharnt be long now, Ben, bor."

"This hare ent Ben, yew silly ow fewl yew," say Mrs. Wicks. "This hare is Harbert."

"Dew yew marry har bor, while yew're got time," say Eli. "She's some woman."

* * *

I stood thare numchance. Mrs Wicks give me a look as she got a bar o' soap an some dwiles out o' har bag but she never say narthin.

"Marry who?" I say.

"Thass right, bor," say Eli. "Dew yew marry har. Only dornt yew never hev no dorters. Dew yew hev a son. He'll join tha Army an go away, an thass tha larst yew'll see o' him. He'll send yew letters – ah, yew'll get plenty o' them. They'll arst for money. 'My boy's in Messerpotearmia,' thass what yew'll tell people when they arst yer. Only if thass a dorter, dew yew drownd it."

"He dew run on," say Mrs. Wicks.

Ow Eli's hand fumbled round till thet hooked hold of another bit o' bread-an-jam an stuck thet in his mouth.

"If thass a dorter," say Eli, "she'll marry some good-fer-narthin an tha pair on em'll set outside yar door an weart for yew to die. They'll watch till yew're abed an then they'll be in an nick yar tea."

"Yew're bin a-talkin to Ben agin, Grandad," say Mrs. Wicks

"I hent got nobodda else to talk tew, hev I?" say Eli. "Anybodda'd think I're got tha whool o' Norwich to talk tew, tha way yew go on. Thass like I say, none on yer never come nare me, exceptin to nick my tea."

* * *

"Now dornt yew be so silly, Grandad," say Mrs. Wicks, shiftin tha ow milk-bottles an junk orf o' tha tearble. "Yew set thare a-talkin to Ben, what a bin dead an gorn this I dornt know how many yare. Lift yar cup up a minnit till I got yar tearble down. Why yew coun't weart five minnits till I got hare an mearde yer a proper cup o' tea I dornt know. But no, yew hatta dew things yar own way, dornt yer?"

"Thet thare tea-caddy wor full Tewsda," say Eli. "Thare ent above fower spoonfuls in it now. Whare dew thet go, thass what I want to know, whare dew thet go?"

"Yew say tha searme week arter week," say Mrs Wicks. "Yew dornt know how tha days go, thass yar trouble."

"Yew tell Millie to mind I dornt ketch har at it," say Eli.

"Yew will hev thass Millie, on't yer,' say Mrs. Wicks. "How many times dew I hatta tell yer Millie is along o' Ben? Go on, yew can put yar cup down now. Look. I're browt yew some more tea, like I allers dew. I'll put thet in tha caddy for yer. See? Now thass gotta larst a week. Nobodda on't come an nick it."

"They'd nick tha house if they could tearke it away," say Eli.

"They're nicked harf on it already. Whare dew thet door go? Eh? Whare dew thet go? Thet dornt go nowhare."

"Thass no good a-tellin on him," say Mrs. Wicks. "Thet thare harf o' tha cottidge wor sealed orf cos thet ent searfe for him. But he carnt unnerstand."

* * *

"Pore ow Bob Blewitt wor tha searme afore he went," I say. "They nearled a door up in his cottidge, an he reckoned he see thet open an thare wor men in a fild cuttin barley."

"Keep yew still now, Grandad," say Mrs. Wicks, "cos I'm a-goin to dew tha floor."

"Yew want to put me in tha wark-house an tearke all whass left," say Eli.

"We'll hatta staart thinkin about suffin afore yew're much older," say Mrs. Wicks. "Yew ent searfe to be left alone."

"Yew're took harf tha house an now yew want tha other harf," say Eli.

"I spose he think I'm Millie, now," say Mrs. Wicks

She tipped tha water out o' the kettle inter tha bucket an staarted a-scrubbin tha floor.

"Thet wor nice on yer to bring him a cabbidge, Harbert," she say. "Dew yew leave it an I'll cook thet for him."

I got on my bike an went back hoom. Like I say, thass proper pittiful to git old.

HARBERT
14th August, 1964

MA AND FANNY GITTIN AT IT

Thare ent no tew ways about it, I'll hatter dew suffin about my Ma an ow Fanny Frorst. Them tew ow gals, they live on their own next door to one another, an they git on one another's narves. Talk about tha autumn o' life, thass more like Maarch winds when them tew fly at one another's troots.

We hent got no rume for my Ma whare we live, an if we did dew, she woun't cume. Old as what they are an marters to tha rewmatticks, they on't budge an inch, neither one on em.

Tha other night when I went round to my Ma's to tearke har a fowl, she met me at har front gearte.

"My hart, I'm glad to see yew," she say. "Tha ow fewl she're gorn out."

"Who a gorn out?" I arst.

"Why SHE hev," say my Ma. "Fanny Frorst hev. Dew we git a muve on we'll jest hev time afore she come back."

"Hev time for what?" I arst.

"Silly ow fewl, I dornt know what a got intew har," say my Ma. "She git warse as she git older. Set in har kitchen mornin, nune an night, an then all of a sudden she up an stick har hat on an out she go."

* * *

"Whass funny about thet then?" I arst.

"Yew dornt know har like what I dew, else yew woun't arst me whass funny about it," say my Ma. "Lor, she hent bin out o' har house for weeks. I see har a-fussickin about in har gaarden one mornin, an thass all. She's goin funny in tha hid, thass har trouble. But we hent got no time to stand hare a-maardlin, not if we dornt want har to ketch us afore we're done.'

"Afore we're done what?" I arst.

"Why, got my screwdriver back out o' har kitchen drawer," say my Ma. "Yar legs are younger'n mine, yew can hop trew har pantry winder. I wor jest a-goin to hev a go myself when yew tarned up."

"Whass yar screwdriver a-dewin on in har kitchen drawer then?" I arst.

"Yew may well arst," say my Ma. "Thass what I're wanted to know this laarst fower month or more. I keep on at her about it – 'When are yew a-goin to give me my screwdriver back?' I keep on a-sayin to her – but dew she tearke a bit o' notice o' me? No, thet she dornt. Next thing is, she'll be tellin me thet thare screwdriver belong to HAR. She'd lie har way out o' gaol, she would."

"Hang on a minnit," I say. "Yew want me to shin up inter har pantry an whip thet thare screwdriver out o' har drawer. Am I right?"

"Thet on't tearke yew as long as what thet'd tearke me," say my Ma.

"Consarn it all," I say. "thet'd be brearkin an entrin."

* * *

"I might a known thet'd be tha arnser I'd git," say my Ma. "Ever since yew took up with thet thare gal Alice, yew hent hed a thowt to spare for yar mother. Yew're like all tha rest on em today, yew hent got no gratitewde."

"Thet hent got narthin to dew with gratitewde," I say. "Only if she go an lodge a complearnt to P.C. Bumble I'll look a duzzy fewl, on't I?"

"Stand out o' my light then," say my Ma, shovin parst me up Fanny Frorst's front parth an mearkin a bee-line for har pantry winder. "If yew want a thing dewin, dew thet yarself. Yew carnt rely on yar kith an kin, thass one thing's sartain."

"Come yew back," I sung out, "yew'll hart yarself if yew imitearte to clamber in thet thare winder."

"A lot yew care about thet, dornt yer," say my Ma, fangin hold o' tha winder-sill an stickin har foot on a flower-pot. Thet'd jest amuse yew to see yar ow mother fall down an brearke har leg."

"Oh, alright. Come out o' tha way, then," I say "I'll nip in an git yar duzzy ow screwdriver – only dew yew stand thare an watch tha rood, cos if she come back I dornt want har to ketch me at it."

"Thass a good boy," say my Ma. "I knew yew woun't let yar ow mother down."

Thet dint tearke me a minnit to git in tha pantry winder an I wor out agin with thet thare screwdriver afore yew could say knife. My Ma fanged hold on it, an pressed thet up agin har chest as if thet wor suffin preshus.

* * *

"She on't git thet in a hurry agin," she say. "Tha wicked ow thing. She on't never got narthin more out o' me, not if she go down on har bended knees she on't. If I hed all tha sorspans an fryin-pans she're borrered orf o' me an never give back, I woun't hev no rume for em in my kitchen."

"Well, thass thet, then, ent it," I say. "Now tha quicker we git out o' har yaard tha better, dew yew arst me."

"Hold yew haard a minnit," say my Ma. "Now we're got tha screwdriver, thet on't tearke no time at al."

"What on't?" I arst.

"Why lettin my pore ow cat out o' har shud," say my Ma. "Whadda yew think I wor so desperit to git my screwdriver back for? Thet ent tha walue on it I'm worried about. Thass my pore ow cat – tha wicked ow dollop, she're hed thet locked in har shud for days. Here, dew yew tearke tha screwdriver – yar hands are stronger than mine – yew can hev thet thare padlock orf in a jiffy."

"Are yew sartain tha ow cat is in thare?" I arst. "I mean to say, this hare time o' yare, yew never know whare an ow cat git tew. They go roamin round for miles arter other cats."

* * *

"Thass right, tearke ow Fanny's paart agin yar own mother," say my Ma. "Thass all what I can expeck. If yew hed a ounce o' feelin for yar pore ow mother yew'd hev thet thare lock orf 'stead o' standing thare tellin me to my hid I'm a liar."

I spose I'm sorft-harted enough to a done what she wanted , only jest then thare wor a yowlin an a scufflin an tew ow tom cats staarted snizzlin round arter each other all over my Ma's gaarden.

"I'll lay one o' them cats is yars," I say.

"Thare he be," sung out my Ma. "Tom! Tom! Come yew on hoom, Tom! Jest look at him, pore ow thing – thin as a rearke and haarf his fur missin! He must a scratched his way out o' har shud. I'll give har a funny ow mobbin when I see har!"

Thet worn't no good me imiteartin to tell my Ma har ow cat wor in a rare ow steart on account o' he'd bin away fightin other ow tom cats for days. When I give har tha fowl an slung my hook, she wor still hollerin about what she'd tell ow Fanny Frorst next time they met.

HARBERT
14th July, 1967

A RARE ARGY-BARGY AT THA W.I.

Accordin to what tha gal Alice say, them wimmen at tha Wimmen's Institewte hed jest got to tha top noot o' 'Jerusalem' when haarf a duzzen on em shruck.

"Jerooooooooo!" they sung out an mizzled orf in all direckshuns.

Ow Mother Quail banged on tha desk with har shewtin stick an wor jest a-goin to holler for order when she chearnged har mind an let out a howl instead.

Tha next thing tha gal Alice see wor Ow Mother Quail up on top o' tha desk holdin har skart up around har knees.

Then she found out what wor causin tha uproar. Thare must a bin a score or more o' mice rushin about all over tha floor. Leastways, thass what she reckon, but she dint stop to count em afore she jumped on top o' tha desk along o' Ow Mother Quail, an by this time moost o' tha wimmen wor up on desks an cubbords theirselves.

* * *

"Git them mice out o' hare!" shaarmed out Ow Mother Quail, but she never done narthin to git rid on em harself.

"I dornt know whass tha matter with some o' yew wimmen," muttered ow Mrs. Wicks, fangin hold of a broom. "Terrified of a few little ow mice – yew want to be ashearmed o' yarselves."

She lunged at a mouse with this hare broom an thet run up tha handle. "Aaaaaarrrggghhh!" she shruck, an wor up on a book-shelf like greased lightnin. She on't never got nobodda to believe har agin when she complearn about har artheritis.

Thet took a minnit or tew for all them mice to disappare inter tha woodwark, an then tha argy-bargy staarted.

* * *

"Somebodda done it deliberit," say Ow Mother Quail, "an I want to know who."

"Yew ent accusin none o' us, are yer, Ma'am?" say ow Mrs. Wicks, "cos if yew are, I shall hev suffin to say about it."

"Thass a wicked suggestion, with all due respeck, Ma'am," say Mrs. Walpole. "Thare ent a member present what can stick tha sight o' mice any more'n what yew can, an anybodda what can say one on us brung them thare mice in for a joke dornt know what they're talkin about."

"Fiddlesticks," say Ow Mother Quail. "Thare's plenty o' pearple in this hare willage what a got their knife inter tha Wimmen's Institewte – an some members what I could menshun what woun't be above stoopin to a low trick like this hare jest to git their own back. This hare's tha wark o' some woman with a grudge – an like I say afore, I want to know who."

"Oooooh!" say ow Mrs. Wicks, what can smell a skandle a mile orf.

"Yew may well say 'Oooooh'," say Mrs. Forster. "I notice yew dint look all thet sarprised when yew see tha whool plearce crawlin with mice."

"Why, yew evil-tongued ow dollop, yew!" sung out Mrs. Wicks. "Yew want to be careful what yew say, else I might let slip a few remaarks about tha time yar sister run orf with a commarshal traveller. This I will say, he picked tha right sister – he'd a hatta be blind to run orf with yew."

"Oooh, did yew ever!" say Mrs. Forster. "Jest lissen to tha wicked woman. How she can stand thare an say them things when thet tearke tha coal-marchant an hour to deliver har coal, is more'n what I'll ever know."

"Now, now leardies, come come," say tha Wicar's missis. "We mussan't luse our tempers, must we. What Mrs. Quail meant to say – if she'll paarden me for presumin to speak on har behaarf – wor simply thet them mice dint git in hare by acksident. Tha question is, how did they git in hare?"

"Thass right," say Mrs. Fletcher, "how did they? We wor all a-standin hare singin one minnit, an tha next they wor all over everawhare. Thet coun't a bin none o' us what let em loose. Dew yew arst me, some kid hulled em in at tha winder."

"I never see no kid hull narthin," say Mrs. Forster.

"Yew woun't would yer?" say Mrs. Fletcher. "Yew hed yar back to tha winder, an so did the rest on us. Thass to say, all barrin yew, Mrs. Quail, beggin yar paarden."

"An Mrs. Runter-Seede," say Mrs. Wicks. "She wor playin tha pianner."

"Hhrrrrmmph," say Ow Mother Quail. "Fearcin tha winder I may a bin, but I hed my eyes fixed on tha ceilin at tha time, like I allers dew when I'm singin "Jerusalem'. I ent in tha habit o' keepin a shaarp look-out for boys with mice when I'm singin tha anthem."

*　*　*

"Thare yew are, then," say Mrs. Fletcher. "Some young warmint what hent got narthin better to dew than run round frightenin tha life out o' his betters hulled them mice in when we wornt lookin."

"Plorsible, I grant yew," say Ow Mother Quail, wearvin har shewtin stick. "But what I want to know is, who put him up to it?"

"Aaah!" say Mrs. Forster.

"Oooooh!" say Mrs. Wicks.

"Mrs. Hooper ent hare tonight," say Mrs. Walpole.

Thare wornt a deen for a minnit.

"Whare is she?"" arst Mrs. Quail.

Them wimmen all looked at one another, as if Mrs. Hooper might a bin hidin in somebodda's pocket.

"I hent sin har all tha week," say Mrs. Wicks.

"Nor yit hint I, and I dornt want tew," say Mrs. Fletcher.

"She's a funny woman when she like," say Mrs. Johnson.

"Look at tha way she carried on arter we hed thet hullabaloo about…" say Mrs. Shank.

Ow Mother Quail corfed loud an clare. "Never mind about tha hullabaloo," she sung out. "As far as what I'm consarned, any parst disagreement in this hare Institewte is all over an done with, an I sharnt thank anybodda what imitearte to dredge thet all up agin. My one consarn is to git to tha bottom o' this hare mouse bisness – an when I say thass one o' tha moost disgreaceful things I're ever come acrorst in all my long yares with tha Institewte, yew'll understand why I insist thet tha culprit a gotta be brought to book."

Well, thet ent no good yew arstin me who hulled them thare mice at them wimmen. All I know is, tha way their tongues a bin a-waggin ever since, thare ent many pearple in Dumpton what ent hed their carrickters blackened. An some offishal from Flitmarsh a bin hangin round tha skewl for days roustin them mice out.

HARBERT
25th August, 1967

THA REF HED HED TEW MUCH

One way an another tha Wanderers a hed a bad staart to tha season. We're only scored one goal – an we woun't a scored thet if tha Diddlin Parva goalie hent a went an walked over tha line by mistearke arter pickin tha ball up.

Mind yew, we did score fower in our gearme agin tha Dedley Resarves, but they reckon tha result o' thet thare match on't count cos tha ref wor drunk.

I never see narthin like thet thare ref – a titchy little feller by tha nearme o' Plunkett from Swidgethorpe St. Mary.

* * *

We hent haardly staarted to kick tha ball about for a waarm-up afore tha gearme, when he come roarin on to tha medder a-blowin his whissel.

"Whass tha matter with HIM?" arst tha boy Chaarlie.

"Dornt tearke no notice on him," say Fred Johnson, our captin. "He thinks hisself somebody every time he blow his whissel."

Howsomever, this hare ref kept on a-darncin about an pointin to tha senter-spot, an tha row he mearde on thet thare whissel wor enough to set all tha dorgs orf baarkin for miles round.

"Give us a charnce, ref," sung out Fred.

"Consarn it, we ent all on tha fild yit," hollered Joe Wilberforce, whass skipper o' tha Dedley Resarves.

Tha ref run haarf-a-duzzen yaards in our direckshun, tripped over his feet, an went down swop on his snout. Then he gathered hisself up an run arter Joe Wilberforce, blowin his whissel as he went.

*   *   *

"Did I hare yew answer me back?" he say to Joe.

"I woun't be sarprised," say Joe.

"When I order tha gearme to staart, thet staart," say tha ref. "And when I order thet to stop, thet stop."

"Use some sense, ref," say Joe. "We carnt staart till we're all on tha fild, can we? What about all them fellers now comin in thare trew tha gearte."

"Right," say tha ref, gittin his book out. "Arnserin back tha ref – impartinence on tha fild o' play – I shall hatta arst yew for yar nearme."

"Stoon me," say Joe, "an tha gearme hent staarted yit."

"Whass goin on?" arst Fred Johnson, what hed run down tha other end o' tha fild when he see tha argy-bargy.

"Dew yew keep out on it," say tha ref. "I'll talk to yew in a minnit." Ow Joe Wilberforce grinned. "I'm hevin my nearme took," he say.

"What already?" say Fred.

"Thass enough o' thet," say tha ref. "I'll tearke yars as well time I'm at it."

*   *   *

By this time we wor all standin round to watch tha fun.

"I'll tell yew what, ref," say young Frank Shank. "Why dornt yew tearke all our nearmes an hev done with it?"

Tha way tha ref slewed round an shearped up at young Frank, I could a swore he wor a-goin to woller him. His ow fearce blew up to twice its size like a duzzy balloon. But jest when I wor expectin him to let fly, he stuck his whissel in his gob an staarted to blow it agin. Then he tarned an run to tha senter-spot, blowin all tha way.

"Come on," say Fred, "we might as well git staarted."

"If yew say so," say Joe Wilberforce. "But I dornt know how far we shall git – thet thare ref, he's springy."

"They reckon his brother got married this mornin," say one o' tha Dedley fellers, "so all he're hed for his dinner, dew yew arst me, is a bottle o' whiskey."

"More like a barrel," say Fred. "Still thare, thet ent narthin to dew with us – thass for tha League secketary to sort out. Come yew on. then – tha way he's a-blowin thet thare whissel, he'll quackle hisself if we dornt kick orf."

* * *

Well, we kicked orf alright, but tha minnit he see tha ball a-rollin, tha ref blew up for a foul.

"Whose ball?" sung out Fred.

"To heck if I know," say Joe Wilberforce. "Yew're narest, so yew'd best kick it."

Fred took tha free-kick, an thass whare we all mearde our fust mistearke. Tha Dedley Resarves rushed up tha fild to wark tha orf-side trap, an we all rushed up tha fild on tha attack. Afore yew could say Jack Robinson, we wor all in their haarf an they wor all in our haarf. Corse, tha ref blew his whissel agin.

"Orfside," he sung out.

"Who is?" arst Fred.

"HE is," shaarmed out tha ref.

"WHO, HIM?" hollered Joe Wilberforce. "Dornt talk sorft – he's our goalie,"

"Go yew on, bor, tearke a free-kick," say Fred to Joe Wilberforce. "I're hed one kick for narthin – now I reckon thass yar tarn."

"Lor, bor," say Joe, "this hare's a-goin to be a rum ow gearme an no mistearke."

* * *

Thet WOR a rum ow gearme an all. Tha whissel went evera ten seckonds. Yew coun't touch tha ball without yew got pulled up for dearngerous play. Haarf tha time tha players wor scared to hit tha ball at all, for fear

139

o' kickin tha ref in tha snout, cos he follered thet thare ball like a dorg follerin a rabbit an he run with his skull bent down as if he coun't see tha ball without he wor six inches away from it.

Twice arly on Fred Johnson an Joe Wilberforce hed a bit of a mardle an discussed packin it in, but they desided to carry on till arter tha interval.

"All this hare runnin about," say Fred, "thet'll freshen him up, he'll be alright in tha seckond haarf. If we refuse to play on, thare'll be a proper ow rumpus, an he might git struck orf. I dornt know about yew, but I dornt want to spoil a feller's charnces jest cos once in his lifetime he hev a drop tew much to drink on his brother's weddin-day."

We fixed tha ref up with a good hot cup o' tea in tha interval an away we went agin.

$$* \quad * \quad *$$

Arter another ten minnits, durin which time Frank Shank an Bartie Tarner hed hed their nearmes took for tha ninth time an tree o' tha Dedley players hed bin sent orf tha fild, we could see ow Plunkett wor gittin warse instead o' better. In tha finish he looked at his watch an blew full-time when we'd only been playin a quarter of an hour.

"All's well what end well," say Joe Wilberforce.

"Thet might a done tha trick but as thet tarned out, thet dint," say Humpty Potter.

"What might a done tha trick?" arst Fred Johnson.

"I slipped a hair o' tha dorg what bit him inter his tea," say Humpty, "but thet never done done him no good."

HARBERT
6th October, 1967

CHAARLIE'S POCKET PICKED

Yew never see such a black eye as what tha boy Charlie hed when he come inter tha Fox tha other night.

"My hart alive, bor," say Fred Johnson, "whare'd yew git thet thare eye?"

"Down south," say tha boy Chaarlie.

"What down thare tha other side o' London, whare yew went to dew a job for Walpole?" arst Tom Drew.

"Thass right," say Chaarlie, what wark for Walpole, tha faarmer.

"Who done it?" arst Enoch Fletcher.

"A duzzy pickpocket," say Chaarlie. "Or a policeman. I dornt know which. I tell yer, they're a rum ow lot down south."

We coun't git a lor more out on him till he'd hed a pint or tew. But arter Fred Johnson staarted a-twittin him for lettin some feller give him a black eye, a huddren greart lout like him what should a bin earble to look arter hisself, tha boy Chaarlie put his pint down.

*　*　*

"Yew can laarf all yew like," he say. "Yew'd be laarfin on tha other side o' yar dial if yew'd a bin in my plearce. How many times a yew hed yar pocket picked?"

"Never," say Fred.

"Well then," say tha boy Chaarlie."A lot yew know about it dornt yer. Hare's me sarnterin up tha rood one minnit, mindin my own matters, an tha next thare's this feller runnin orf with all my money.

"Thet wornt what he done," he say. "thet wor tha narsty way what he done it. I mean to say, we wor miles out in tha country at tha time.

"Tha marster sent me down south with a sealed onvelope for some faarmer called Robinson at a willage called Bundley. He reckoned thet wor important bisness an he dint trust tha poost with it an he coun't go hisself, so he arst me to go, cos he wanted this hare onvelope put inter Robinson's hand.

"Well thare, I dint mind a day out at Walpole's expense, so orf I searled. When I got to tha stearshun at tha other end, I arst how to git to Bundley, an they told me thet wor tree mile up tha rood an thare worn't another bus for an hour-an-a-haarf, so I thowt I might as well walk.

"I give this hare onvelope to Robinson an staarted to walk back to tha stearshun. Thass when this totty little ow witterer come up to me an staarted to walk alongside.

" 'Hello, my boy,' he say. 'Thass nice to hev company along tha rood, now ent it?'

"I sized him up an I dint like him. For tew pins I'd a telled him to sling his hook. But thass a bit of a rum ow job when thare's only tha tew on yer in sight, an yew're booth goin tha searme way down a long rood. So I telled myself I'd hatta put up with him.

"I woun't a minded if he hent a bin such a proper ow woman. He kept a-frearmin on about narthin till yew'd a thowt his tongue'd wore itself out. Tha way he kept a-fangin hold o' my sleeve, an stickin his snout inter my cheek as if he wor short-sighted, thet proper mearde my skin crawl.

* * *

"Then all of a sudden when we come to a side rood he say 'Well cheerio then, my boy,' he say, an away up this hare side rood he went.

"Tha minnit he'd gorn I sort o' felt suspishus. I'd got my money in a wallet in my inside pocket, an my retarn ticket as well. Suffin mearde me lay a hand on my pocket – but thet fared as if tha wallet wor still in it.

"I dornt know why, but I still wornt satisfied. I tarned thet thare pocket out – an thet wornt my wallet in it at all, thet wor one o' them little ow pearper bags like they keep money in at them banks an thet wor stuffed with newspearper.

"My hart, I wor riled, I can tell yer. Mind yew, I coun't help admirin tha crarfty way what he'd bin an took my wallet out an shoved thet thare bag in without me knowin narthin about it. Howsomever, I wor up thet thare side rood arter him like a dorg arter a rabbit.

" 'Yew thievin warmint, yew,' I say. 'Dew yew give me my wallet back. I carnt git hoom without my retarn ticket.'

"He give me a look as if he wor a-goin to bust out howlin.

" 'My boy, my boy,' he say, 'dornt brearke an ow man's hart. We hed such a friendly walk together along tha way. Thet'll hart my feelins if I think yew think I'm a thief.'

"Thet got my monkey up more than ever, thet did, an I give tha warmint a piece o' my mind. Then when he see I meant to git my wallet back even if I hed to twilt him good an proper to dew it, he telled me he wor right disappointed in me cos he took me for a friendly young feller, an now thet looked as if I wor jest another one o' them young hooligans what'd meet an ow man on a country rood an whip his money orf on him.

* * *

"Tha long and tha short on it is, we hed a bit of a scuffle, an seein as I dint like to hit him with all my force, I fanged hold on him an put him acrorst my showlders like what they call tha fireman's lift.

" 'Alright,' I say, 'either yew give me my wallet back, else I'll carry yew to tha narest policeman an give yew in chaarge.'

"An orf I went up tha rood torrards tha town with this hare feller on my back.

"He wor as light as a feather at fust but arter he'd a-riggled about a bit an spent ten minnits or more runnin on about me hartin his feelins, I begun to wish I hent done it. Then I see tha town ahid, an I thowt thet woun't be long afore I found a policeman an then…"

"Hang on a minnit," say Tom Drew. "Why tha hike dint yew jest hold him down an sarch his pockets an nip yar wallet back?"

"Thass what I should a done, I reckon," say tha boy Chaarlie. "But by tha time I did think o' dewin it, my knees wor thet fagged out , I dint think I'd hev tha strength to run arter him quick enough if he got away.

"Howsomever, we come to tha town in tha finish, an I staarted lookin round for a policeman. Corse, when yew dornt want to see one, thare's a duzzen on em behind yer. Thare wor me with this pickpocket weighin a ton an I coun't see one nowhare."

"Did yew find one in tha finish?" arst Fred.

"Find one?" say tha boy Chaarlie. "I come round a corner an run inter about twenty. Thare they all stood, some leanin up agin tha wall, others in tews an trees a-mardlin. 'Hey!' I hollered, hullin tha ow man down in tha middle on em. 'This feller's a pickpocket. He knicked my wallet. Dew yew tearke him in chaarge.'"

* * *

"So thet tarned out alright then," say Enoch Fletcher.

"I hent finished yit," say Chaarlie. "Them policemen wornt policemen at all. They wor duzzy actors. Thet fared as if a fillum company wor mearkin a fillum. Yew should a hud tha hullabaloo when I maarched in!

"Some feller hollered, 'Cut!' an come roarin up to me, wearvin his aarms about, an a couple o' them so-called cops fanged hold o'me, an

143

out o' tha corner o' my eye I see tha pickpocket sneakin away, an thass when I went shanny.

"I dornt know exackly what happened in tha next couple o' minnits, but tha next thing I did know I wor standin thare with my wallet in my hand, thare wor bits o' fillum camera layin about all over tha shop, haarf a duzzen o' them policemen wor stretched out on tha rood, an tha rest wor mizzlin orf round tha corner a-hollerin blew marder.

"I dint see much sense in hangin about so I nipped orf down to tha stearshun right shaarp an come hoom. All I can say is, thet ent no good yew arstin me who give me this hare black eye, cos I dornt know.

HARBERT
10th January, 1969

WHERE THA BANK MONEY IS HID

"Thare's a lot o'pearple round hare'd git a shock if they knew all what I know," say Ow Dan Forster, fangin hold o' Fred Johnson's beer an swallerin haarf on it afore Fred see him.

"Hare we go agin," say Tom Drew, tha landlord.

"I mean it," say Ow Dan. "I could tell em a thing or tew about how some o' tha bigwigs round hare got their money – an thet'd give em a shock, I can tell yer."

"What, like ow Brigadeer Bloodulf, and Harbuckle at tha Maltins, or who?" arst tha boy Chaarlie.

"Bigger men than them," say Ow Dan. "Only if yew think I'm a-goin to nearme nearmes, yew're got anothin think a-comin. I're known fellers end up in gaol jest fer nearmin nearmes."

"Ow Dan hent never bin to gaol in his life," say Tom Drew, givin us a grin.

* * *

"An I dornt fancy goin now," say Ow Dan. "So thass why I keep myself to myself. I're lived tew long an sin tew much for some pearple's likin.

I reckon I know more about tha Flitmarsh bank robbery than what tha police ever found out."

"Git away," say Enoch Fletcher.

"Thass a year or tew ago now, Dan," say Tom Drew.

"Ah, thass several yare ago," say Ow Dan, "but to my sartain nollodge tha feller what done it is one o' tha biggest men in these hare paarts today. Yew'd never believe me if I telled yer his nearme. He worn't a Norfolk man – he come from away somewhare. He wor jest a thievin young rarscal in them days, an he got in with some gang what found out how much money parssed trew tha Flitmarsh bank.

"All yew want is a good haarvest an thass a maarvel how much money git left at tha bank by all tha ow faarmers from miles around. This hare gang picked tha right day, whipped in quick, an away they went with a hunderd thousand pound.

"Yew remember thet thare bank robbery, Tom, thet wor in all tha pearpers at tha time…"

"And they never did ketch tha gang what done it," say Tom Drew.

"Now yew're a-comin tew it," say Ow Dan. "Tha gang split up an went in diffrent direckshuns. But for one reason or another all tha money wor in a tin box in a car what this hare feller I'm a-talkin about drive away in.

"His idea wor to git a few miles out o' Flitmarsh, bury tha box at a spot what he'd picked for tha job, an then come back for it arter a week or tew when all tha fuss hed died down.

"Well, thass what he done – only he never come back for it cos he wor nicked by tha police round London way for some barglery what he'd done months afore."

"How dew yew know?" arst Enoch Fletcher.

* * *

"Never yew mind how I know," said Ow Dan. "I know what I know, an thass all thare is about it. Fower yares haard learbour he got sentenced tew, an all tha time he wor thinkin o' tha day when he'd git out an dig thet thare box up.

"In tha finish he wor a free man agin, an tha fust thing he done wor git hisself a car an mizzle orf up to whare he'd buried tha box.

"Thass when he got a shock what tarned out to be tha biggest tarnin

145

-point in his life. Tha spinney what he'd bin an buried tha box in wornt thare.

"He wor proper frantick for a bit – he went roarin round thinkin he might a mearde a mistearke about whare thet lay on tha map, but thet wor tha right plearce an thare wornt no gittin away from it.

"He went all hot an cold as he stood thare a-gaarpin – cos whare thet thare spinney hed bin they'd built a factery. Thet hed gorn up time he wor in gaol. Thare wor fower foot o' concrete over tha box. An on top o' thet thare wor machinery.

* * *

"I know tha factery yew mean," say Tom Drew.

"I'll lay yew dornt," say Ow Dan. "Howsomever, this hare feller kept tellin hisself they must a found tha box time they wor diggin tha foundearshuns but he coun't be sartain. For one thing thet'd a bin all tha pearpers an he'd a got to know about it. Tha more he hung about round tha factery tha more he mearde his mind up tha box wor still down thare, right underneath tha factery floor.

"Thet begun to prey on his mind suffin crewel. He'd got a forchune buried right under his snout an he coun't git at it. Thare wornt no charnce o' him burrerr-in under tha factery, nor yit diggin down trew tha floor, not with warkmen thare day an night. Besides thet'd a took a small army o' men a week to dew tha job.

"Still, he coun't bear tha thowt o' tha money bein lorst for good. An then thet struck him – tha one man what could dig thet up an no questions arst wor him what owned tha factery.

"He went away an set hisself up as a scrap metal dealer in tha Midlands for a staart. Bit by bit he done well an then he bowt up a small engineerin bisness what used tha scrap. He warked hisself like a madman, cos all tha time he wor thinkin o' tha box full o' money.

"Arter about ten yare he owned a duzzy greart chearn o' foundries an metal warks an one thing an another all up an down tha country. He wor a big man by then, tha sort what kept gittin his picksher in tha pearpers, playin golf with fillum stars or out shewtin with politishuns.

"An thass when he took over tha factery nare Flitmarsh, along with a lot more. He built hisself a house close by, an when he ent livin in London, thass whare yew'll find him. So now yew know werra nigh as much as what I dew."

146

"I spose he dug up tha money then?" say Fred Johnson.

"My hart alive, bor," say Ow Dan. "No thet he dint. A big man like him, thass tha larst thing he wanted to dew. He're got wealth, he're got posishun, an if he carnt sleep at night thass on account o' hevin nightmares about what might happen if tha box come to light an they find his fingerprints on it, an conneck him with it, an dig up his parst an send him orf to gaol agin.

* * *

"I tell yer, he staarted out wantin tha factery so as he could dig tha money up, but he ended up wantin tha factery so as nobodda woun't never dig tha money up, not in his lifetime."

Ow Dan drunk up an went.

"Yew dornt want to tearke no notice on him," say Tom Drew. "Thare ent a ward o' trewth in tha yaarns what he spin."

"I know thet," say tha boy Chaarlie. "But I woun't mind bein left alone in thet thare factery for a week with a newmattick drill an a shovel."

HARBERT
24th January, 1969

SOFTLY, SOFTLY IN HOLEY SOCKS

P.C. BUMBLE dint say narthin time he carst his ow glimmers acrorst tha hidlines in tha newspearper.

But when he got to a bit about ten thousan quid's warth o' brandy bein nicked orf of a lorry, he let out a row like a kettle a-bilin over.

"Whadda yew ail, bor?" arst his missis. "Are yew a-sickenin for suffin or what?"

"Lor, mor," say Bumble, "on't they never larn no diffrent?"

"On't who never larn no diffrent?" arst his missis.

"Why, them willans what nick things orf o' lorries," say Bumble.

147

"They're jest arstin to be run in haarf tha time. They're got that whool organisearshun o' tha law agin em, thass what they're got."

* * *

"Hhmmmph," say Mrs. Bumble. "An when did yew larst run one on em in?"

"Arter they're nicked ten thousan quid's warth o' brandy they're got to git rid on it, this whare thet come in," say Bumble."How are they a-goin to get rid o' ten thousan quid's worth o' brandy without us a-knowin about it?"

"I can think o' ways," say his missis.

"Oh, can yer," say Bumble. "Then all I can say is, thass a good job for yew yew're married to me an not to them."

"So long as thare's fellers about like Humpty Potter," say Mrs. Bumble, "they can allers git rid on it."

Bumble stopped with a spoonful o' porridge haarfway tew his gob an give his missis a look.

"Ah," she say, "yew dint think o' Humpty, did yer. Tha times yew're bin up all night imiteartin to ketch him for next to narthin, an then when thare's a proper big job done yew set thare like a lump o' wood an forgit all about him. I tell yer, if they ever mearke yew a sargent thet'll be a mirackle."

"Fetch me my bewts, missis," say Bumble.

* * *

Tha fust thing he done wor shaarpen his pensil, then he stuck his nootbook in his pocket an took a squint at tha silver watch his farther left him, jest to mearke sartain o' tha time. He allers carry thet thare watch, cos he reckon thet keep better time than tha one what he carry offishal.

"Ten thousan quid's warth o' brandy," he say tew hisself as he stuck his bike behind tha hedge oppersite Humpty's. "Thet'd be warth a bit o' promoshun to me if he're got some on it hid away in his shud."

He took a peark inter Humpty's yaard but he coun't see narthin.

"Thare's times." he say tew hisself, "when a bard in tha hand is warth tew in tha bush, an tha only way to git it is to ignore tha correck prosedure. Warrant or no warrant, without I sarch these hare premmises I might as well go hoom agin an wearve thet thare brandy goodbye."

Inter Humpty's yaard he hopped, an he wor haarfway to thet shud

148

when a thowt jumped inter his skull. How thet found enough rume in his skull is beyond my know, but thass what thet done.

"Consarn it," he say tew hisself, "I carnt go scrunchin acrorst all this hare gravel in these hare bewts without he'll hare me."

"Thet dint tearke him more'n another five minnits to realise thet tha best thing what he could dew wor tearke his bewts orf.

Howsomever, once he got em orf thet wor a rum ow job knowin what to dew with em. Thet wornt no good a-carryin on em in his hand, cos he wanted his hands free, an when he tied tha learces together an slung em round his neck they mearde his chest all mucky. Besides, they kept on a-goin clump-clump right under his snout, an on top o' thet he dint like tha smell on em.

* * *

In tha finish he stood his bewts down by one corner o' tha shud time he sneaked up an took a squint trew tha winder.

Thet took a while for his glimmers to get used to tha daark inside tha shud, an when they did dew, he mearde out a few bottles in one corner, but he coun't tell what wor in em. He wor jest a-mearkin up his mind to open tha shud door when he hud a woice right behind him.

"Mornin, Superintendent," thet say.

He slewed round sharp, an thare stood Humpty.

"Nice mornin, marster," say Humpty.

"Fiffppppibit," say Bumble.

"Narthin like a bit o' fresh air for coolin tha feet," say Humpty.

"I dornt want none o' yar lip, Potter," say Bumble, drorin hisself up an dewin his best to look diggernified.

"Yew want to git yar missis to daarn them socks, bor," say Humpty. "Yar big toes'll ketch their death o' cold."

"Yew weart till I git my bewts on," say Bumble. "I're got a few things to say to yew."

"Bewts?" say Humpty. "What bewts?"

"Why, them bewts what – stoon me, they're gorn!" sung out Bumble. "What a yew bin an done with my bewts, Potter? They stood thare jest a minnit ago!"

* * *

"I never see no bewts," say Humpty. "Yew're sartain yew feel alright?"

149

"If yew dornt give me them bewts afore I count tree, Potter," say Bumble, "yew'll wish yew hent never bin born."

"Are yew sure yew hed them on when yew left hoom?" arst Humpty.

"Let me remind yew, Potter," say Bumble, "stealin a policeman's bewts is a sarious offence agin tha law. Either yew hand em over or yew go to jail, whichever yew want."

"Talk sense," say Humpty. "How could I a nicked yar bewts, a big feller like yew? My hart alive, yew're twice tha size o' me. How could I a overpowered yew an dragged yar bewts orf? Tha Bench woun't never believe it."

"Consarn it, I TOOK em orf," hollered Bumble.

"Tha Bench woun't never believe thet neither," say Humpty. "I ent all thet sure I believe it, myself. I mean to say, I know thare's times when yew act a bit peculiar for a policeman, but goin round parsewin yar inquiries in broad daylight in yar stockinged feet? Blow me, if yew wor to stand up an say a thing like thet thare in Court, they'd laarf thet loud yew'd hare em all tha way to Norwich."

"I want them bewts," say Bumble.

"Forgitful, thass what yew are," say Humpty. "I'll lay if yew nip hoom an arst yar missis she'll tell yer yew left in such a hurry yew forgot to put em on."

* * *

Tha more Bumble weighed thet up, tha less he liked tha idea o' tellin his sargent he'd hed his bewts nicked by Humpty Potter, let alone gittin up in Court an tellin tha Bench.

An seein as he coun't find them bewts nowhare, no matter whare he looked, he dint hev no opshun in tha finish but to git on his bike an mizzle orf hoom. with his big toes stuck out, one on each side, like a couple o' spuds.

"Whare tha hike are yar bewts?" arst his missis.

"I left em at tha cobbler's," say Bumble. "They wanted mendin."

HARBERT
15th October, 1971

THASS A FIDDLE ON THA ORGAN

Yew might a wondered what Ow Dan Forster wor up tew tha other night. Dew yew'd a bin thare yew'd a sin him sarnter inter tha charch with a bundle o' ow newspearpers, a box o' matches, a pair o' bellers, an a cat.

Tha thing is he'd orfered to git tha mice out o' tha organ, an the Wicar wor only tew pleased to let him git on with it.

Them mice what nest in tha organ, they're a proper newsance. Thare's enough noots on thet thare organ what on't play already, an I reckon about another fower a conked out since larst Chrissmas.

* * *

Ow Dan telled tha Wicar tha best thing to dew with them thare mice wor smook em out, else thet woun't never play proper. So thass how he come to unscrew tha front, set light to bits o' pearper, an blow tha smook trew with them bellers.

He woun't tell us what he'd bin an soaked tha pearper in, cos he reckoned thet wor a trearde secret, but I must eay thet mearde a marster lot o' greasy ow smook. He knelt thare a-corfin an a-splutterin for I dornt know how long, a-puffin away with them bellers, an evera time a mouse run out his ow cat wor on it like a rocket. They ended up with a duzzen dead mice betwixt em.

Mice is what I call em, only Ow Dan, him bein as old as tha hills, he call em 'meezen'."

Mind yew, he duzzy nare set fire to tha organ a couple o' times, an thet woun't a sarprised me if tha Wicar hed a hed a hart attack if he'd a bin thare. But he stayed away, an thet wor tha best thing dew yew arst me, cos he's thet tender-harted tha sight o' tha ow cat a-pouncin on them mice would a killed bim.

Arter thet wor all over his missis went an tried tha organ out to see if thet'd play any better, but she hed a fearce as long as a fiddle when she come hoom.

* * *

"Rearly, Charles," she say to tha Wicar, "we'll hatta git a new organ, thare ent no tew ways about it."

"As sune as what we can, my dare, we will," say tha Wicar. "But yew know what thass bin like imiteartin to rearse tha money this larst 20 yare."

"Yes, I know," say his missis, "but if we dornt rearse it quick we might jest as well hev no organ at all. Thet sound horrible."

" 'Sing unto him a new song: play skillfully with a loud noise' – Psalms 33-3," say tha Wicar.

"A loud noise is right," say his missis. "Thet mearke more noise than mewsick, thet pore ow organ dew. Thass why I hatta play it myself – we carnt git no proper organist to come an play it no more."

"An a werra good job yew mearke on it, my dare," say tha Wicar. "I hent never hud what yew call a proper organist play a better tune on it than what yew dew."

"I dornt git no pleasure out on it, thass a sure thing," say his missis. "Tearke larst Sunda – yew would go an pick 'Tha Charch's One Foundearshun' for tha fust hymn."

"An a splendid hymn thet is," say tha Wicar.

"So thet may be," say his missis. "But with them tew noots up thet end o' tha keyboard what dornt dew narthin but let out a grunt like an ow sow with har snout in tha troff thet come out o' thet thare organ like 'Tha Charch's PLONK Foundear-PLONK.' All thet done wor rewin tha sarvice."

* * *

"Praps yew could put thet up a noot next time,"say' tha Wicar.

"One noot woun't be enough," say his missis. "Thet'd only mearke matters warse, cos then yew'd hev 'PLONK-PLONK-PLONK one PLONK-PLONK shun'."

"Ah," say tha Wicar, "then what about mearkin thet tew noots higher? Thet oughter dew tha trick."

"Thet might dew tha trick so far as what tha organ's consarned," say his missis, "but I hearte to think o' tha effeck thet'd hev on tha congregearshun."

"I dornt git yar drift," say tha Wicar.

"Why," say his missis, "haarf o' them ow men sing in their bewts already. Yew try an git them to sing tew noots higher an thet'd be a mirackle if they dint bust a blood wessel."

"Oh," say tha Wicar.

"I ent sayin they woun't dew their best," say his missis, "But even if they dint dew

theirselves a injury, tha result'd sound more like a hard o' cows a-bellerin for their calves than a congregearshun a-singin a hymn."

"I see," say the Wicar. "What yew mean is, thet'd be better to hev tha organ mearkin a noise like an ow sow than hev tha congregearshun mearkin a noise like a hard o' cows? One good country noise instead of another."

"If thass tha way yew want to put it," say his missis, "then yes, I spose thass about tha size on it."

"Tha only altarnative," say tha Wicar, "is a new organ, an thass suffin what we're a-goin to hev to weart a long time for."

"We're bin weartin a long time as thet is," say his missis. "Yare arter yare we run ewents for tha organ fund, but thet dornt fare to be gittin us nowhare."

"Tha trouble with tha organ fund," say tha Wicar, "is thet thass like Achilles an tha tortus." (I dornt know who this hare Achilles might a bin – thet ent a Dumpton nearme I dew know – but thass tha way yew spell it, so tha Wicar reckon.)

"Achilles kept on a-runnin to ketch tha tortus," say tha Wicar, "but evera time he got to whare tha tortus hed bin, thet'd muved on a bit in tha meantime, so he never ketched thet in tha finish."

"I carnt think why he wanted tew," say his missis.

"Thass tha searme with tha organ fund," say tha Wicar. "Evera time we git enough money in tha fund, to buy an organ, tha price o' organs a gorn up so we're still short."

"We're got enough in tha fund now," he say, "to a bowt tew organs at tha price they wor fetchin when we staarted. By this time next yare we oughter hev enough to buy one at tha price they are now – but they'll a gorn up agin by then, or I'm a Dutchman, an we'll still be fifta pound light."

"Parss me my mewsick," say his missis. "I've an idea I'd miss some o' them dud noots if I wor to play 'Tha Charch's One Foundearshun' in tha key o' B flat."

HARBERT,
22nd October, 1971

153

GHOOST OF A TREE IN A HOWLIN BLIZZARD

"Tha only ghoost what I ever see," say Tom Drew, tha landlord, "wor tha ghoost of a tree."

"Ghoost of a what?" arst Fred Johnson.

"A tree," say Tom. "A big ow beech tree."

"Git away," say tha boy Chaarlie. "Trees dornt hev ghoosts."

"Thass all yew know about it," say Tom. "Dew I hare any more orders?"

We all got Tom to pull us another pint apiece cos we dint want to go dry time he stood thare a-popplin on about this hare ghoost.

"An thet wor tha only ghoost what yew ever see – this hare beech tree?" say Enoch Fletcher.

"Thass right," say Tom. "Without yew count what I see a-hangin from it."

* * *

Thare wornt a deen for a minnit, apaart from Enoch a-swallerin – he's a noisy swallerer, Enoch is – as we set thare with our ow glimmers on Tom, a-weartin for him to tell us.

"I wornt all thet old at tha time," say Tom. "Earteen, nineteen – I carnt remember for sartain. I could wark thet out if I could remember what yare we hed tha blizzard when that snow lay haarfway up pearple's winders. Ow Dan hare, he remembers thet yare, dornt yer, Dan?"

"Ah," say Ow Dan Forster.

"Thet wor a crewel yare for gittin about," run on Tom. "All tha roods wor blocked. Tha faarmers lorst a lot o' their stock in tha drifts, cos thet come on so sudden. An cold! Some o' tha old uns what dint hev enough wood to barn got took orf by tha cold, pore ow devils, an thet wor a funny ow job a-tryin to bury em.

"I wor a-courtin a mawther at Fumbleham at that time," he say, a-lowerin his voice an pearkin over his showlder, as much as to say, I dornt want my missis to hare this bit. "Tha snow wor wearst high as I blundered acrorst tha filds,an thet took a bit o' gittin thare. But thet wornt narthin compared with gittin back, cos thet wor pitch daark by then, an thet hed snew haard all tha artunune, so yew coun't tell which wor tha hedges, let alone tha roods.

"Thet wor tha sort o' night when yew could a friz to dead on yar own doorstep without knowin tha house wor thare. Thet wornt long afore I wor lorst – an when I say lorst, I mean it. I could a bin in tha middle o' Walpole's ten-acre or I could a bin at tha North Pool for all tha difference I could see."

*　*　*

"I know how yew mean," say Fred. "I once strayed orf tha Diddlin rood on a dark night an coun't find my way back agin. I coun't even see tha tellagraarf pools."

"Thare must a bin a bit o' light from somewhare," say Tom, "cos jest for a step or tew all round me tha snow glimmered whitish, but thass as far as thet went. I dint know which way I wor a-goin, or which way I oughter be a-goin, or if I wor a-goin round in sarcles. I did think once I come acrorst some holes in tha snow what I must a mearde myself, but I coun't be sartain. All what I could dew wor keep on a-goin, an I kept on a-goin for hours.

"If I could a sin tha lights o' Fumbleham I'd a gorn back, but tha snow wer thet thick I coun't see narthin. Tha warst on it wor tha wind – thet blew suffin crewel, an in tha finish I wor worn out with it.

"Thare hent bin many times in my life," say Tom, "when I thowt I wor a-goin to die, but this hare wor one on em. I kept on a-tellin myself if I stopped I'd fall down an never git up agin. I reckon one thing what kept me a-goin wor thinkin how shanny thet'd be to conk out haarfway betwixt Fumbleham an Dumpton. If thet'd a bin tha Artic or somewhare thet'd a bin different, but to git lorst an die o' cold in a plearce what yew're known since yew wor so high, thet dornt mearke sense, dew it?

"Howsomever thet duzzy nare come to thet in tha finish. I wor a-blunderin about, at my wit's end, when I ketched my foot in a brarnch of a fallen tree what wor buried in tha snow, an as I pitched forrard I hit my hid haard agin suffin. Thet knocked me clean out, an tha next thing I knew I wor laying thare in tha snow, an I dint know if I wor alive or dead.

"I dint know whare I wor, or how I got thare, or what I wor a-dewin thare, an I coun't haardly remember my own nearme. I dint know whare I'd bin or whare I wor a-goin. Thet wor all a blank. I felt more surprised than anything, cos I coun't think why I'd wook up an found myself layin thare cold an weak in tha middle of a howlin blizzard, in tha pitch daark, with a pearn in my skull like somebodda wor a-hittin on it with a hammer.

"Then I looked up an see tha tree. Not tha one what I'd blundered intew under tha snow, but a big ow beech tree praps a farlong away up tha sloop. I dint think to wonder why I could see it like I could, when I coun't see narthin else for tha snow an tha daark, but thare thet stood, as plearn as day, a big tall tree with snow on tha bare branches

* * *

"I remember thinkin to myself, thass tha tree on tha top o' tha Beacon Hill, an if I can git tew it, all I're gotta dew is go down thet hill inter Dumpton.

"I up an away, like a new man, an thet dint tearke me long to reach tha tree. Thass a good job, I remember tellin myself, thet I know thet thare tree well. Thass searved my life, thet thare tree hev, I kept a-sayin.

"As I parssed under it, I see one thing what I sort o' haarf expected. Thet wor a-danglin from a bough – a suffin shearped like a man, all wound up in chearns, an thet wor a-swingin backards an forrards in tha wind . I could hare thet a-creakin as I parssed.

"Thet must a stopped snowin by then , cos once I wor parst tha tree I could seen tha lights o' Dumpton at tha bottom o' tha Beacon Hill, an I wor thet glad to be hoom I haarf run, haarf scrambled all tha way down."

"Hold yew on a minnit, ow paartner." say tha boy Chaarlie. "Thare ent no tree on tha top o' Beacon Hill."

"Thass jest it," say Tom. "But accordin to what tha old uns say, thare must a bin a tree thare once. Thass whare they used to hang tha highwaymen."

HARBERT
10th December, 1971

HOLLERIN AN' HOWLIN AN' DANGLIN

My hart alive, yew should a sin tha boy Fred Johnson when he come drollerchin inter tha Fox tha other night.

He looked a proper downpin, thet he did, an arter about five pints he

156

telled us why. Stoon me, we hully did laarf. We dint oughter a done, I spose, but we coun't help it.

Thet wor all on account o' his missis.Yew know har – tha gal Jinny – har proper nearme wor Giannina when she fust come round this way, cos she wor an Eyetalian what come to wark for Ow Mother Quail up at tha Hall, but Jinny'a what she're bin called ever since.

She fare to hev a pair o' ear-rings – greart ow things like cartain-rings with red stoons in, what must a bin handed down to har in har famila.

I're sin har wear them charnce-time when tha sun is hot. I dorn't know if a bit o' sun an blew sky mearke har happy, thinkin she's back hoom whare she come from or what. Praps thass why she wear em on a fine summer's day thow why thet should mearke her happy rememberin whare she come from is beyond my know, seein as har famila wor right pore. By what Fred say, her father dornt hev narthin but a few acre o' stoons an a dickey. But yew carnt tell with wimmen.

* * *

Howsomever, Jinny'd got them ear-rings on when he come hoom from wark one day larst week, an she wor a-smilin to harself an lookin ten yare younger.

Tha fust thing what fleu inter his mind wor seein tha coal marchant up tha end o' thet rood as he wor on his way hoom.

He're brook more wimmin's harts round hare , hev thet thare coal marchant than my dorg a got fleas. A hansom-lookin feller he is, I're gotta admit, with a big black mustash, thow I woun't like to say if thass black by nearture or jest git thet culler on account o' his trearde.

"Hev tha coal-man bin?" arst the boy Fred, tearkin a good squint at them ear-rings.

"Corse-a he bin," say tha gal Jinny.

"Did yew know he wor a-comin?" arst Fred.

"Corse-a I knew he wor a-comin," say Jinny.

"Is thet why yew put them ear-rings on?" arst Fred.

Well arter she'd stopped a-hollerin at him, an he'd took his fingers out o' his lugs, he hed another go.

"Alright then, what ARE yew a-wearin on em for?" he arst.

"Thass-a my bisness," say Jinny. "I can-a wear-a them if I like-a."

"What, for dewin tha housewark in?" say Fred.

157

"Why-a not?" say Jinny. "I wear-a them cos it may be tha larst-a chance I git to wear-a them."

"Whadda yew mean by thet, then mor?" arst Fred.

"We not-a git-a much money," say Jinny. "All-a tha prices they go up. All-a tha money, yew spend at the pub. Whare-a we git clothes for tha children? Praps-a tomorrow I must-a sell-a my ear-rings."

* * *

Tha boy Fred coun't help thinkin about it arterwards. He dint know what to believe. One way or tha other, thet wor a rum ow job.

Tha way he looked at it, she might a took a fancy to tha coal marchant, an if so he'd hatta put a stop tew it. Then agin, she might a meant what she said about sellin them ear-rings an thet wor suffin he coun't bear to think about, cos she wor right fond on em. Besides, they wor warth a lot more'n what she'd git for em.

In tha finnish he mearde his mind up. Tha next mornin, he whipped them ear-rings out o' tha drawer an hid em.

He never hud no more for a day or tew. Then on tha Frida night when he come hoom she give him a funny mobbin.

"Hold yew yar duller, mor, dew," he say. "Whadda yew at, now?"

"My ear-rings!" she shruck. "What-a yew dew with them?"

"Me?" say Fred.

"Yes, yew," she sung out. "I know what-a yew dew with them! Yew sell-a them and spend-a tha money in tha Fox!"

Fred reckon he wor proper flummoxed. Thet wor suffin what he hent expected. He set thare stammed an dint know what to say.

"Thass a shearmeful thing what-a yew done," she run on. "All-a yew think about is-a beer. Yew not-a think about me an my children. We can-a staarve an yew not-a care. Yew tearke-a my ear-rings from-a my drawer, an yew sell-a them to git-a money for yarself."

"I never done narthin o' tha sort," say Fred. "Yew're bin an hid em somewhare an carnt find em, thass all."

Thet set har on agin good an proper, an when she'd done she bust out howling.

She kept on at him all tha evenin, an he dint git no peace at breakfus tha nexter mornin, an thet went on like thet thare till he shoved orf for tha cricket match agin Diddlin Parva. He wor right orf form, I can tell yer, an we lorst by a mile.

158

By tha end o' tha gearme Fred'd mearde his mind up thet when he got hoom he'd hatta slip them ear-rings back in tha drawer an mearke sartain she found em, else his life'd be a misery.

But when he got hoom he got more than what he bargained for.

"I'm back, mor," he sung out. "Let's be hevin a bit o" grub."

She set thare in tha kitchen chair an never muved a mussel.

"Yew not-a git no grub," she said

"Whass thet yew say?" he shaarmed out.

"I say yew not-a git no grub," she say.

He stood thare with his gob open, an then he see she'd got a pair o' greart ow ear-rings a-danglin from har lugs, only they wornt har old uns, they wor a diffrent shearpe an a sort o' greenish blew.

"Whare'd yew git them ear-rings?" he say.

"I went-a to Flitmarsh an bowt em," she say.

"Bowt em?" he sung out. "Whare'd yew git tha money from?"

"Whare-a yew think?" say Jinny. "Yew drink-a my ear-rings – alright. I git-a myself some more an now yew not-a eat-a no grub cos I wear-a next week's grub on my ears. If yew not-a like, I go away an not-a come back."

Corse, he telled har what he'd done an imitearted to mearke a laarf on it, but she dint think thet wor funny, an she wor still a-keepin on him on short rashuns when he telled us about it in tha Fox.

HARBERT
28 July, 1972

THA SILVER ONE THET ENT RED

Thet thare perfessor Morfrey looked a proper job as he stood thare in tha witness box at tha Flitmarsh Court, with his red fearce an his bald hid an glarsses like jam-jars.

Yew should a sin his snout twitch when ow Mr. Lucas Miffler, tha chareman o' tha Bench, pulled him up shaarp.

"Consarn it all," say Mr. Miffler, "what this hare Court is a-dealin with this mornin is a cairse agin Paul Wigstone Pounce for keepin a dorg without a dorg licence. We dornt want to hare narthin about no Skandinearvian natcheralist – whass his name – Lynn suffin or other?"

"Linnaeus, yar warship," say Perfessor Morfrey.

"Thass right, Lynn Ayers," say Mr. Miffler. "Well, like I say, without he's bein called as a witness in this hare cairse, anything he're gotta say about it ent narthin but haresay."

* * *

"May thet please yar warships," sung out Mr. Jellicoe Hickey, o' Stot an Hickey, what wor thare for tha defense, "thet might be difficult to call Linnaeus as a witness on account o' he died about a couple o' senturies ago."

"All tha more reason for leavin him out on it," say Mr. Miffler.

"As yar warship please," say Mr. Hickey. "Now then, Perfessor Morfrey, in accordance with tha rulin o' tha Bench, praps yew could leave Linnaeus out on it while yew tell us why Pounce's dorg ent a dorg but a fox"

"I'll dew my best," say tha Perfessor, givin ow Mr. Miffler a look fit to tarn him inter a frog. An then he larnched hisself inter a riggermarole what wor thet full o' long wards I hed to arst him arterwards how to spell em, an if I hent got em right, thass his fault, thet ent mine.

"Tha thing is," he say, "tha fox wor considered by tha arly natcheralists to belong to tha dorg familia, or Canidae..."

"Can he die?" arst Elijah Frogg, him what they call Fresher.

"Exackly," say tha Perfessor.

"C-a-n-h-e-d-i-e," say Fresher, a-scratchin on it down with tha rest o' his noots on tha back of a dutty ow onweloop. "Alright, dew yew go ahud, ow paartner."

"For thet reason," say tha Perfessor, "tha fust nearme given to tha fox wor Canis vulpes."

I must say thet sounded like "wool-peas" to me, an so thet must a done to tha Bench, cos Fresher Frogg wor on tew him like a rocket.

"Cans o' what?" he arst.

"Wool-peas," say tha Perfessor.

"What tha hike are wool-peas?" arst Fresher. "They're a new un on me. I thowt I knew suffin about peas, seein as my cuzzen mearke a good

160

livin a-growin on em for Bards Eye, but I hent never hud o' wool-peas. Hev yew, Miffler?"

"No, thet I hent," say Mr. Miffler, "but we're gotta give tha witness credit for knowin what he's a-slaverin on about. Alright, Perfessor, dew yew carry on, only jest remember, tha quicker yew spit thet out, tha quicker we can all git hoom whare thass warm."

"With tha Court's parmishun," sung out Mr. Hickey, "may I submit thet we shall all git hoom a lot quicker if tha witness is allowed to give his evidence without no more inneruckshuns?"

"Thass what I're bin a-sayin all along, ent it?" say Mr. Miffler.

"I'm much obliged," say Mr. Hickey. "Well now, Perfessor, what thet come down tew is thet foxes used to be clarssed as dorgs. But would I be right in assumin thet science tearke a diffrent view nowadays?"

"Yew would an yew woun't," say ow Morfrey. "Broadly speakin, they still belong to tha dorg famila, but modern science lump tha fox an other speshies relearted to it inter a genus on their own, tha genus Vulpes. So tha typical fox ent called Canis vulpes no more, thass called Vulpes vulpes."

* * *

"This hare git warse an warse!" sung out Mr. Miffler. "Consarn it all, we come hare this mornin to deal with a dorg licence, not to lissen tew a lot o' squit about wool-peas-wool-peas!"

"May thet please yar warships," say Mr. Hickey. "I must arst yew to bear with tha witness a little longer. Unless I'm much mistook, he's about tew explearn to yar satisfackshun exackly how a fox differ from a dorg within tha meanin o' tha Act."

"Quite so," say Perfessor Morfrey. "As yar warships will readily appreshiearte, tha nearsal passidges of a fox dornt open inter holler spearces in tha frontal boons, like what they dew in a dorg. Whass more, as I'm sure yar warships know, tha poost-orbital processes of a fox are flat or hollered, while a dorg's are conwex."

"Dang my jacket!" hollered Mr. Miffler. "This hare ent narthin but a load o' gibberish! What tha hike a wool-peas-wool-peas an holler boons got to dew with tha cairse? Dew yew mean to stand thare an say a willage constable dornt know a dorg when he see one?"

"Did tha constable examine tha animal's nearsal passidges an poost-orbital processes?" arst Perfessor Morfrey.

"My hart alive, whadda yew tearke him for, a simpleton?" shaarmed out Mr. Miffler. "If a willage constable want to know why a feller hent got a licence for his dorg, he dornt go a-pawkin up its snout, dew he?"

"In this instance, yar warships, thet might a bin a good idea if he hed a done," say tha Perfessor.

* * *

"I never hud such a tarradiddle in all my born days," say Mr. Miffler. "Pounce's dorg a bin described on ooth as a greyish-black with a bit o' white in it, an we all know foxes are red."

"Yar warships," say Perfessor Morfrey, "thare are many distink warieties o' foxes. Thare's Vulpes vulpes leocopus, thare's Vulpes vulpes montana, thare's Vulpes vulpes aegyptica, thare's..."

"Thare's a hoom for mental cairses at Dingham Sorshways, an if this hare go on much longer we'll all be in," shruck Mr. Miffler. "I're hed about as much wool-peas-wool-peas as what I can stand for one mornin. Without we git a bit o' concrete evidence consarnin Pounce's dorg, I sharnt want to hare no more."

"Praps I can be of assistance to tha Bench," say Mr. Hickey. "What Perfessor Morfrey's a-gittin at is thet tha so-called silver fox, as yar warships will know, ent red at all, thass black sprinkled with white."

Thare wornt a deen for a minnit.

"Thass right enough, come to think on it," say Fresher Frogg in tha finish. "My niece hed a coller mearde o' silver fox."

"Thare wor a feller what bred em at one time round Fumbleham way," say Buncombe.

Ow Mr. Miffler pulled his mustash. Then him an his feller magistreartes staarted a-marmerin among theirselves. But I'll hatta weart till arter Chrissmas now afore I let yer know how tha cairse ended.

HARBERT
15th December, 1978

HARBERT'S CHRISTMAS SPECIAL
NO SIGN SO FAR OF THA LONELY OW FELLER

This hare Chrissmas is diffrent from other Chrissmases, on account o' we hent sin narthin yit o' Bygone Nicholas.

I dornt know why they call him Bygone, nor yit if his proper nearme is Nicholas, but thass what he're allers bin known as in these hare paarts for as long as what I can remember.

Thass tha kids what allers watch out for him. In tha week afore Chrissmas, yew'll see them young 'uns a-standin thare by tha green, a-pearkin up tha rood parst tha charch, an then one day yew'll hare one on em holler: "Hare he come! Hare come ow Bygone Nicholas!"

An then all tha kids mizzle orf to meet him as he come a-sploddin along, with his ow sack on his back, an his white beard a-blowin in tha wind, an his fearce as red as a brick.

* * *

Mind yew, when I wor a young un his beard wor black. Then as tha yares went by thet got grey strearks in it. Now thass as white as snow, an so are his teeth when he grin, but thass on account o' they're false uns.

Why he come to Dumpton at Chrissmas is beyond my know. He allers did tell us he come to spend Chrissmas with his Arntie. But he sleep in a derelick cottidge on Walpole's land up tha Diddlin rood, what hent bin touched since tha rufe fell in afore tha tha Fust Warld War, an thare ent narthin in thare but rats.

I once arst Ow Dan Forster if he knew anything about Bygone Nicholas's Arntie, cos if thare's anybodda what dew know, thet'd be Ow Dan. But he reckoned he dint.

"Thare wor a woman lived in thet thare cottidge afore tha Fust Warld War, thet I dew remember," he say. "A bit light in tha hid she wor, an all, pore ow thing. An I did see a boy thare now an agin, if I remember right, but whare he come from, an if he wor har neffew, thass suffin what I carnt say."

* * *

One thing about ow Bygone Nicholas, he's a marster with a jack-knife. Give him a lump o' firewood, and he'll caarve yew anything yew want.

I're got windmills at hoom now what he mearde for me when I wor a young un.

Tha larst time I see him wor jest afore Chrissmas larst yare, as I wor a-parssin tha green. Thare he set, with a greart ow red coot an hood on like what them yachtsmen wear – anneracks I believe they call em – an what with his white whiskers an his red cheeks an his wellinton bewts, he looked as if he wor all dolled up ready to nip down somebodda's chimney.

Thare wor a haarf a duzzen little mawthers round him, about six or seven yare old I reckon, an tha one he wor a-talkin tew wor young Annie Wicks.

"Whass yar nearme, then, little un?" he say.

" Annie," she say.

"So thass Annie, is it?" he say. "Thass a nice nearme, thet is. Dornt yew think thass a nice nearme?"

Young Annie sort o' smiled a bit, but she never say narthing.

"My nearme's Nicholas, mine is," he say. "Yew can call me Nicholas if yew want. I're come to spend Chrissmas with my Arntie, hent I."

"Whare dew yar Arntie live then?" arst young Annie.

"Ah, well now, thet'd be tellin, woun't it?" say Bygone Nicholas. "I mean to say, my Arntie might not like it, might she. Dew I went and telled yer whare she live, she might give me a funny ow mobbin."

* * *

He screwed his ow glimmers up an let out a laarf, an then he picked up an ow bit o' wood what laid thare alongside his feet.

"Hello," he say. "Thare's suffin inside this hare wood. Can yew see suffin inside this hare wood?"

All them kids laarfed, an young Annie say, "Corse not," she say. "Thass jest a lump o' wood, thare ent not narthin inside it."

"Ah, but thare is," say Bygone Nicholas. "I can see thet clare. Go yew on with yer, yew can see thet an all, carnt yer?"

Them kids all gaarped for a minnit, afore they laarfed agin, like as if they wor in tew minds about it, an coun't be sartain if they'd sin suffin or not.

"Whatever can thet be, I wonder," sa Bygone Nicholas. "I know, I'll git my ow jack-knife out an let thet loose. Thass all thet want – thass shut up in this hare lump o' wood, pore thing, an thet want me to let thet out."

164

He hacked a bit of a notch at one end o' tha wood an stuck his glimmer tew it. Then he got young Annie to stick har glimmer tew it.

"Thare yew are, what did I tell yer?" he say. "Yew can see suffin in thare now carn't yer?"

"Corse I carn't,' say young Annie.

"Corse yew can," say Bygone Nicholas. "An what dew yew think thet is?"

"I dornt know," say Annie

* * *

"Why, thass a little animal, thass what thet is," he say. "Pore little ow thing, thet must be a little mouse, I reckon. No, hold yew haard, let's hev another look. Why, my hart alive, thass a little rabbit. Shall I let thet out?"

"Yes!" hollered all them kids.

"Alright then," he say, a-whittlin away at tha wood. "Now let's see if we can find it."

Arter about a minnit he held tha wood up an sung out: "Look! Thass a-staartin to come out! Thass got one lug loose already. I'm right, ent I? Thass a little ow rabbit's lug, ent it?"

"Oh, ah!" hollered them kids. An they wornt far out neither, cos tha bit o' wood what stuck out at one end did fare to look like a rabbit's lug.

"Alright, then," say Bygone Nicholas. "Shall we let tha rest on it out?"

"Yes, yes, yes!" hollered them kids.

"Now, young Annie, yew'll hatta promise me suffin," he say. "Dew I let this little ow rabbit out o' tha wood, pore little thing, whare some nasty ow witch must a shut thet up, yew will look arter thet proper, on't yer?"

"Oh, yes, Mr Nicholas," say young Annie. "Corse I will."

"Yew promise?"

"Oh, yes, Mr Nicholas,"

"Alright, then, I'll tell yew what," say Bygone Nicholas. "Yew see them ducks on tha pond over thare? Well, yew go an count em for me, an then run twice round tha green, an then come back hare an let me know how many ducks thare are, an then if yew're a good gal we'll see about givin yew tha rabbit."

Orf toddled young Annie, an Bygone Nicholas's jack-knife staarted a-chippin away like mad. Shivers o' wood flew in all direckshuns. By tha time young Annie got back, all red in tha fearce an hampered for har breath, thet worn't a lump o' wood in his hand no more, thet wor tha living image of a rabbit, a-crouchin thare with its lugs pressed down on its back an its little ow tearl stuck on behind.

"What did I tell yer?" he sung out. "I knew thare wor a rabbit in this hare wood all along!"

But young Annie staarted to howl.

"I wanted to see thet come out!" she blared. "Yew sent me away, an I wanted to see thet come out!"

"Never yew mind, young un," say Bygone Nicholas. "They're shy, they are, little ow rabbits. They dorn't come out o' their burrers if yew stand thare a-watchin on em, now dew they?"

"No," say young Annie, a-sniffin haard.

"Well, then," he say. "Dew yew tearke thet hoom now an look arter it. An then when pearple arst yew whare yew got it, yew can tell em, carn't yer, thet wor shut up in a lump o' wood an ow Nicholas let thet out."

* * *

Young Annie wiped har snout on one sleeve an har glimmers on tha other, an orf she run with har rabbit without so much as a thankyer. Bygone Nicholas watched har go with a smile.

"Now, then," he say to them other kids, what wor a-jumpin up an down an a-hollerin thet they all wanted one tew, "now let's see if thare's any more animals a-hidin inside them bits o' wood under thet thare tree."

Well, like I say, thet wor tha larst I see on him. I did come parst tha ow derelick cottidge one night, thet wor tha Chrissmas Eve if I remember, an I could a swore I hud woices a-mumblin to one another, an I could a swore one on em wor a woman's. But thet thare cottidge look more like a ruin than ever this Chrissmas an thass as silent as tha grearve.

HARBERT
December 22nd, 1978

EVIDENCE IN COURT IN DORG CAIRSE

One way an another we hed a good Chrissmas an New Yare, an I hoop yew all hed tha searme, but now thass over I can git back to thet thare cairse o' tha dorg an tha dorg licence up tha Flitmarsh Court.

Thet wor tha cairse, if yew remember, whare Paul Wigstone Pounce, what wor chaarged with keepin a dorg without a licence, reckoned his dorg wornt a dorg but a fox.

We left thet, dint we, whare ow Perfessor Morfrey in tha witness-box hed jest reminded tha Bench as how some foxes wornt red, cos tha silver fox wor black sprinkled with white.

Ow Mr. Miffler, tha chairman o' tha Bench, he shot a look at Mr. Jellicoe Hickey, o' Stott an Hickey, what wor thare for tha defense.

"My hart alive," he say, "are yew imiteartin to mearke out as how Pounce's dorg is a silver fox? Cos if yew are, thet tearke a bit o' swallerin."

*   *   *

"May thet please yar warships," say Mr. Hickey, "I suggest we rely for our informearshun about tha nearture o' Pounce's animal on tha evidence o' Perfessor Morfrey, whass an expart in these matters.

"Now Perfessor," he say, "let's clare up one thing for a staart. Would yew, with yar expart nollidge, or would yew not, describe Pounce's animal as a silver fox?"

"Not exackly, yar warships," say Perfessor Morfrey.

"Not exackly!" thundered Mr. Miffler. "What tha hike dew yew mean, not exackly? Is thet a silver fox or ent it?"

"My niece got bit by one o' them," say Elijah Frogg, him what they call Fresher.

"Stoon me, not yar niece agin!" sung out Mr. Miffler. "She's lucky to be alive, yar niece is, dew yew arst me. Thare ent a cairse come up in this hare Court but what yew reckon yar niece a bin barnt tew a sinder, haarf drownded, or biled in oil. She're got more lives than a bloomin ow tom cat, she hev."

"She wor lucky she dint git rearbies," say Buncombe tha corn marchant. "They can give yer rearbies, them foxes can, if they bite yer."

"We could a swore she did hev rearbies at fust," say Fresher. "Har jaw wor locked solid. We hed to whip har orf to tha horspital."

"Yar jaw dornt git locked solid with rearbies," say Buncombe. "Thass lockjaw, thet is."

"Thass what they telled us at tha horspital," say Fresher. "But thet wornt lockjaw neither. What she'd done, she'd bin an picked up tha wrong tube when she wor a-fixin har false teeth in. Har gob wor full o' glue."

*   *   *

"We appare tew a wandered away from tha point o' this hare cairse," cut in little Miss Crimp, what set thare a-diddlin about with har glarsses. "Am I tew unnerstand, when Perfessor Morfrey say Pounce's dorg ent exackly a silver fox, he mean thass somewhare betwixt tha tew?"

"I'm obliged to yar warship," say Mr. Hickey. "Tha possibilita thet a silver fox from tha fox faarm at Fumbleham might a got loose an bred with a dorg at some time or other is sartainly one what tha Bench oughter consider. Now, Perfessor Morfrey, might I arst if such a thing could happen in yar expart opinion?"

"Ah, thare yew hev me," say tha Perfessor. "My reckords shoe as how a crorss betwixt a dorg an a fox a bin reported umpteen times by unqualified passons, but so far as what I know, thare hent never bin no properly orthenticated cairse."

"But thare ent no scientifick reason why thet coun't happen?" arst Mr. Hickey.

"Like I telled tha Bench at tha beginnin," say Perfessor Morfrey, "dorgs an foxes belong, broadly speakin, to tha searme famila, so thare ent no theoretickle objeckshun to crorssin Vulpes vulpes with any member o' tha Canidae."

*   *   *

"Stoon me," sung out Mr. Miffler, "we're back to wool-peas-wool-peas an can-he-die agin. Why tha hike carnt yew larned skollers git down to brarss tacks? Cos if yew mean what I think yew mean, yew mean Pounce's dorg is haarf a dorg an haarf a fox."

"Or tha other way round, yar warships," say Mr. Hickey.

"Ah," say Fresher. "Haarf a fox an haarf a dorg."

"Tha question is which haarf," say Mr. Hickey. "As tha larned clark will confarm, thare ent no provision under tha Act for issuin harf a dorg licence. Parlyment dint allow for tha possibilita thet somebodda might keep haarf a dorg."

"Them M.P.s, they're short-sighted, thass why," say Mr. Miffler. "They never git narthin right, dew yew arst me."

"Thass my opinion," say little Miss Crimp, " as how tha Bench'd be better plearced to deside this hare issue – an arter all, thass us what a gotta mearke our minds up if thass a dorg, or a fox, or haarf an haarf – if Pounce's animal wor perduced in evidence."

"I'm grearteful to yar warship for mearkin thet thare suggestion," say Mr. Hickey, " cos thass jest what I wor a-goin to dew,"

Well, a feller come in with this hare dorg on a lead, an a funnier lookin brute yew never did see. Thet wor long an thin, with a bushy tearl, an like P.C. Bumble hed telled tha Bench, thet wor a sort o' blackish-grey with bits o' white in it. Thet come a-sniffin at tha floor all tha way up to tha Bench, an then thet let out a row like a steam whissel.

* * *

Ow Mr. Miffler gaarped at it with his glimmers a-jumpin out of his skull. Buncombe set thare like a sack o' pig-meal, Miss Crimp polished har glarsses for tha umpteenth time, an Frogg scratched suffin down on tha back o' his dutty ow onweloop.

"Dang my jacket!" sung out Mr. Miffler in tha finish. "If thass a fox I'm a Dutchman, an if thass a dorg I'm a double Dutchman! No, hold yew yar duller, Mr. Stickey, cos if yew set yar witness orf agin, all we'll git is another load o' wool-peas-wool-peas!

"I dornt know what my feller justices think, but I reckon we oughter give yar client tha bennefit o' tha doubt, an hull him an his animal out abroad afore thet bite somebodda. Cairse dismissed!"

"I'm much obliged," say Mr. Hickey.

"All I know is," say Buncombe, "if they want me to buy another dorg licence, they can whissel for it."

"Git away, bor," say Fresher. "Yew're got an Alsearshun, hent yer?"

"Not arter this mornin I hent," say Buncombe. "Thass a wolf."

HARBERT
5th January, 1979

169

SUFFIN UNLUCKY AT THA REARCES

Thare wor a rum sort o' look on Martha Bumble's fearce as she watched har husban, Police-constable Bumble, a-gittin hisself ready to go out.

Fust he shone his bewts up with suffin out of a tin, an then he shone his hair up with suffin out of a bottle. Or thet might a bin tha other way round.

"Stoon me," she say to harself, "he carnt be arter another woman, can he?"

She ran trew a list o' all tha wimmen she knew what might a took his fancy, but coun't think o' none what wor darft enough to mistearke him for Gregory Peck, without thet wor tha barmeard at tha Ticklin Green Man.

Howsomever, tha mistry o' what Bumble wor a-dollin hisself up for wor sune solved when he say, "I spose yew carnt let me hev a few quid out o' tha housekeepin till next week?"

"So thass whare yew're a goin," she say. "I might a known. Yew want to hull tha housekeepin money away on them hosses at the Flitmarsh Pint-to-Pint."

"Whare I'm a goin," say Bumble, "is confidenshal. When a policeman git ordered somewhare on offishal bisness, thet'd be more 'n what his job is warth for him to let on whare he's a-goin. Besides, I ent tha only one. I reckon thare'll be more on us at tha Flitmarssh Pint-to-Pint t'yare than what thare ever hev bin afore."

"Oh? Why?" arst his missis.

"Lor, mor, duzzens on us from all over tha districk a bin called in to lend a hand at tha Pint-to-Pint t'yare," he say. "Judgin by informearshun reseeved, tha Inspeckter reckon tha ground'll be seethin with pickpockets. Tha more uniforms they see a-minglin with tha crowd, tha less likely they'll be to risk dippin their fingers in pearple's pockets."

"Well, I dornt see what yew want tha money for," say Mrs. Bumble. "Yew ent allowed to drink on dewty, so I'll lay you ent allowed to bet on dewty neither. Still thare, if yew want it, I spose yew'd best tearke it."

Me, I reckon Bumble might jest as well not a bothered to shine up his bewts, cos when I see him at tha Pint-to-Pint he wor up tew his ankles in mud an sluss.

Thare wor hunderds if not thousans o' pearple all a-flounderin about when I got thare, and them what wornt up to their ankles in mud an sluss wor up to their knees in it. Tha cars on tha car-paark fared to look as if they'd bin warshed thare by a flood, an thare wor hunderds more cars a-honkin away in the rood outside tha ground, what coun't git in on account o' a lorry wor stuck in tha mud an blockin tha gearteway. I tell yer, thet wor a rum ow job.

* * *

"Thet'll be heavy goin this arternune," say Humpty Potter. "I'd a put my money on Flyblown, dew tha ground hed bin haard, but thare's only one hoss for these har condishuns, and thass Lockjaw."

"I fancy Housemeard's Knee myself," say Enoch Fletcher. "She won hare tha season afore larst."

"Jelly Bean in tha fust rearce an Iron Leardy in tha seckond," say Fred Johnson. "Stoon me, yew coun't arst for a better tip than thet thare, could yew?"

"I carnt see why," say tha boy Chaarlie.

"Nor yit carnt I," say Frank Shank.

"What, with ow Maggie Thatcher jest back from seein tha Yank President?" say Fred. "Consarn it, thet stick out a mile."

"What tha hike a they gotta dew with it?" arst Chaarlie

"Lor, bor, they call har tha Iron Leardy, dornt they?" say Fred. "An him, he eat jelly beans, dornt he? If thet ent a sign from above, I dornt know what is."

"Never mind about signs from above," say Humpty Potter. "An ounce o' inside informearshun is warth a ton o' signs from above, an inside informearshun is what I're got. Dornt never bet on narthin but sartainties is my motter."

"An yew reckon Lockjaw is a sartainty, dew yer?" arst Enoch.

"Thet carnt luse," say Humpty. "I'll tell yew what, dew yew give me a fiver apiece – or a quid apiece if yew carnt afford a fiver – and I'll put thet on for yer when I go to lay my own money on."

"I dornt know," say Fred.

"Thass up to yew," say Humpty. "Corse if yew dornt want to tearke adwantage o' my inside informearshun, thass yar own look-out. All I know is, I only want to dew yew fellers a fearvour on account o' yew're all my meartes from Dumpton. I woun't drearm o' sharin my nollidge with no furriners from nowhare else."

171

Well, we give him our money in tha finish, speshly arter he telled us he'd let us hev thet back if Lockjaw went an lorst. I mean to say, thet wor as good as a garantee.

I never see much o' tha rearce myself. All I see wor a cloud o' mud a-flyin in all direckshuns. But arter thet wor over I arst some feller which hoss hed won, and he say "Flyblown."

"Flyblown?" I say. "Yew mean Lockjaw, dornt yer?"

"Stoon me," he say. "Lockjaw ent a hoss, thass a can o'dorg's meat. Thet run on crutches, thet dew. Both its back legs are tied on with string. Thet'll be Easter Monday afore Lockjaw finish."

We all mizzled orf to find Humpty, but tha larst rearce wor over afore we spotted him.

"My hart alive, we're bin suffin unlucky this arternune, hent we?" he say. "Leastways, I hev, cos on top o' lusin my money I're gotta dip inter my pocket to let yew hev yars back. Pounds thick thet'll corst me. Still thare, a promise is a promise, an I carnt say fairer than thet."

He shelled us our money out, an we felt right sorry for him at tha time. But arter we'd put tew an tew together, we dint know what to feel, cos thass as good as sartain he never bet on Lockjaw at all. What he done wor put all our money on Flyblown, an then bet moost o' tha winnins on Bread Poultice, what romped hoom in tha fowerth rearce at fifta to one, so he must a picked up thosands.

"Well." say Mrs. Bumble when PC. Bumble got hoom. "Did yew ketch any o' them pickpockets?"

"No," say Bumble with a fearce like thunder. "But thare's one o' tha warmints I'd like to lay my hands on. He went an whipped all tha money out o' my pocket. Whass more, he nicked my bloomin whissel as well."

HARBERT
20th March, 1981

FRED FRY'S NEW HID O' HAIR

Laarf – we roared our hids orf in tha Fox tha other night when we hud about Fred Fry at Diddlin Parva a-goin an gittin hisself one o' them hair transplants.

"He hed a hid like an egg larst time I see him," say Tom Drew, tha landlord.

"Well, thet ent like thet now, bor." say Enoch Fletcher. "He're got enough hair to stuff a cushion with. Black as soot thet is an all."

"He want to be careful," say Ow Dan Forster.

We all slewed round an gaarped at Ow Dan, cos he'd bin thet quiet all evenin we'd forgot he wor thare.

"Whadda yew mean, he want to be careful?" arst tha boy Chaarlie.

"What I say," say Ow Dan.

"Dew tha good Lord hed meant him to hev hair, he woun't a gorn bald, would he? Growin other pearple's hair, thass dearngerous thet is."

"I carnt see why," say Fred Johnson.

"Corse thass dearngerous," say Ow Dan. "Yew dornt never know whare other pearple's hair come from, dew yer? Yew could hev a marderer's hair on yar skull for all yew know, coun't yer7 Yew'd be haarf a marderer yarself then, woun't yer? Look what happened to ow Annie Wicks."

"Hare we go agin," say Tom Drew.

* * *

Thet took us about ten minnits to mearke out which Annie Wicks Ow Dan wor a-talkin about, but in tha finish thet tarned out he meant George Wicks's granmother, what died long afore our time.

"Shanny ow woman, she got harself a wig," say Ow Dan. "She coun't a give no more'n sixpence for it, cos if yew want to know whare thet come from, I reckon thet come from tha knacker's yaard. Hoss-hair, thass what we all telled har that looked like. An hoss-hair thet must a bin, cos she staarted eatin oots an jumpin over hedges. When she got so as she kept on a-tellin everabodda she wanted to run in tha Grand Nashunal, they hed to put har away."

"Well, thet ent hoss-hair what ow Fred Fry a got, thass yuman hair," say Enoch Fletcher arter we'd stopped laarfin.

"Thass a duzzy site warse, dew yew arst me," say Ow Dan.

"Whare dew thet come from, thass what I want to know."

"I did read in tha pearper once as how a lot on it come from Italy," say tha boy Chaarlie. "Some o' them Eyetalian mawthers what live on them smallholdins thare, whare they hent got narthin but dickey an a few earcre o' stoons, they let their hair grow long an then sell it to mearke a livin."

"Thare yew are then," say Ow Dan.

"Thet woun't sarprise me," say Fred Johnson, "if some o' them prison baarbers dint dew a trearde in it. When yew think o' all tha long-haired yobbos what go to jail an hev their hair cut short, stoon me, thare must be tons o' hair a-pillin up in them plearces."

"Now yew're a·talkin," say Ow Dan. "Thare wor a feller by tha nearme o' Jackson once lived at Ticklin St. Andrew what went about in a wig. He wor a caarpenter by trearde, but arter he got thet thare wig he hed to give up caarpenterin on account o' he coun't knock a nearl in streart.

"All what he wanted to dew arter thet wor ride motor-bikes. Thet wor as if he wornt tha searme feller al all. Yew'd see him a-tearin round tha learnes on his motor-bike with all tha kids a-hollerin 'Scorcher!' arter him. Thet'd be in tha nineteen-twenties, thet would.

"Corse, we all wondered whare he got tha money from to buy motor-bikes with, an thet wornt long afore we found out. Tha mornin he wor up in tha Flitmarsh Court on fower charges o' barglery, thet wor tha mornin we knew how he mearde his livin.

"His missis, she wor a nice little woman, she coun't mearke hid nor yit tearl on it. 'He hed a good livin as a caarpenter,' she say. 'an then all of a sudden like he fared as if he went shanny. One day he wor good at his job, tha next he wor all fingers and thumbs. One day he wor good-living and kind, tha next he staarted a-knockin me an tha kids about. He wor thet chearnged, dew I'd a met him in tha street I woun't haardly a known him.'

"He wor in jail for I dornt know how long,' say Ow Dan, "an when he come out agin he wornt no diffrent. Thet coun't a bin more'n a fortnight afore he mizzled orf on his motor-bike to rob tha bank in Flitmarsh. He come a-runnin out with tha money and jumped on his motor-bike to git away, but he dint git far. A bunch o' kids hed let tha wind out o' his tires.

"He wor in an out o' jail for months at a time, an in tha finish he went in for good. Thet wor on accouot o' one night he went for his missis with a poker an duzzy nare killed her. Dew tha paarson hent a knocked at tha door jest as he wor a-shearpin up to finish har orf, he'd a bin a job for tha hangman.

"So like I say, Fred Fry want to be careful. Thass my belief thet thare wig what Jackson wore wor mearde from tha hair of a crimminal. Else why should a respeckable caarpenter a gorn tha way he went?"

Ow Dan give us all a look an then swallered his pint.

"Dornt talk so sorft, Dan," say tha boy Chaarlie. "A' feller dornt chearnge on account o' his hair."

"Yew want to read tha Good Book," say Ow Dan. "Yew young uns, yew woun't talk so iggerant dew yew wor to go to charch on Sundays a bit more orfen. Hent yew never hud o' Samson? He wor a big strong feller time he hed his hair, an look what happened to him arter they cut thet orf. I tell yer, tha hair on a man's skull a got a lot to dew with what sort o' life he lead, Thet'll be a rummun if ow Fred Fry dornt find the out."

* * *

Arter Ow Dan hed bid us goodnight an gorn hoom, we hed a bit of a laarf, cos he's a proper ow liar.

Howsomever, suffin Tom Drew telled us did mearke us wonder.

"Thass funny, yew should menshun about a lot o' yuman hair a-comin from Italy," say Tom. "Mind yew, thare carnt be narthin in what Ow Dan wor a-runnin on about, but all tha searme thass a rummun,"

"Whass a rummun?" arst Chaarlie.

"Why, bor," say Tom, "accordin to what I hare, Fred Fry a signed on at a night skewl to larn Eyetalian."

HARBERT
27th March, 1981

BILLY BLEW THA BUGLE

Thare wor a bugle in Billy More-or-Less Hooper's hand when he got up at tha Districk Cownsil meetin tha other day, an afore tha chairman could stop him, he stuck that tew his lips an blowed it.

"Ta-raaaa, ta-raaaaa, toot-toot," thet went.

Tha chairman tarned skaarlet, an brung his hammer down on tha tarble thet haard, all tha water jumped out o' his glarss an soaked tha minnits.

"Consarn it all, Cownsillor Hooper," he shrunk, "what tha hike dew yew think yew're a-dewin on?"

"I'm more or less a-blowin this hare bugle, Mr. Chairman," say ow Billy. "Thare's a few pearple round this hare tearble what more or less want wearkin up."

"Set yew down, Hooper," sung out tha chairman, "yew're out o' order."

"So I may be, Mr. Chairman," say ow Billy, "but this hare bugle ent. Thet more or less blow as loud an clare now as what that did dew afore tha war when tha belonged to tha Territorials."

"Well, yew carn't blow that in hare an thass a fack," say tha chairman. "We ent in tha Territorials now."

"Nor yit ent them pore ow pearple in tha Dedley Ow Pearple's Hoom," say Billy, "but they more or less might jest as well be, tha way they more or less git bossed about. By an large, thaas why I come to what I might call a momentary decision, to more or less blow revally on this hare bugle at this hare Cownsil meetin, in tha arnest an more or less effulgent hope thet blowin this hare bugle might more or less wearke a few on yer up to tha skanderlous way them pore ow pearple are more or less trearted. Tearkin one thing with another ... "

"Quiet. carn't yer!"shaarmed out tha chairman. "Stoon me, Hooper, yew're bin a member o' this hare Cownsil long enough to know yew carnt jest git on yar hind legs an popple on about suffin what dornt appare in tha minnits. Yew can go trew tha minnits with a fine-tewthed coomb till yew're blew in tha fearce, an yew on't find narthin about tha Dedley Ow Pearple's Hoom in em nowhare."

* * *

"Thankyer for yar timely support, Mr. Chairman," say ow Billy. "I'm more or less greartful tew yer for pointin out to this hare Cownsil tha werra thing what I wor a-comin tew next. Like yew more or less say, Mr. Chairman, thare ent narthin about tha Dedley Ow Pearple's Hoom in tha minnits, an – to my mind, lookin at it all round, an tearkin tha rough with tha smewth, thass what I might call tha biggest cryin skandle o' tha sentury.

"Yare in an yare out, in fair weather or foul, this hare Cownsil more or less meet in tha full diggernity an tarpitude o' what I might call its civic pride, an never a ward git spook about tha Dedley Ow Pearple's Hoom, whass more or less a blot on tha fair fearce o' this hare districk.

"May I more or less remind yew, Mr. Chairman, an all them honnerable an warshipful members o' this august body what set hare a-noddin orf round this hare tearble, may I remind yew as how them pore ow pearple a reached tha evenin o' life's day arter long yares o' warkin their fingers to tha boon for tha bennefit o' what I might call mankind, only to find when tha sheardes o' night more or less begin to fall…"

"Hull him out abroad, Mr. Chairman," sung out Cownsillor Hardbuckle.

* * *

"Thass all werra well for tha Harbuckles o' this hare warld, Mr. Chairman," run on ow Billy. "They're got their shares in tha Flitmarsh maltins to more or less keep em in luxury. But what a them pore ow pearple got in tha Dedley Ow Pearple's Hoom? I'll more or less tell yer what they're got – they hent got narthin.   .

"Arter a lifetime o' what I might call toil, yew might think a pore ow man or a pore ow woman more or less desarved a bit o' comfort in tha sunset o' their yares. An what dew they git? They git bossed about from mornin till night. They ent cared for – they're jest whipped out o' bed, fed, an whipped back agin, for all tha warld as if they wor battery hins stead o' granfars an granmothers what a done good sarvice to tha communita.

"As for tha food, all what they git is a saample for their breakfus, an another saample for their dinner, an another saample for their supper, an thet more or less never chearnge from one day to tha next, till them pore ow pearple git fed up to tha back teeth with it, or would dew if they more or less hed any back teeth left.

* * *

"Thass like when we hed all thet thare whalemeat durin tha war – whalemeat today an whalemeat tomorrer till we wor more or less sick on it.

"Thet thare Vera Lynn even sung a song about it, dint she…"

"For tha larst time, Hooper," hollered tha Chairman, "are yew a-goin to set down or ent yer? Tha Dedley Ow Pearple's Hoom hent got narthin to dew with this hare meetin, an nor hev Vera Lynn. Anyhow, I dornt know what song yew're a-slaverin on about."

"Thet more or less went like this hare, Mr. Chairman," say ow Billy, a-clarin his troot an a-bustin inter song. "Wha-a-alemeat agin, dornt know whare, dornt know when …" An he give another tootle on his bugle an set down.

HARBERT
29th May, 1981

OW DAN PLAY AGIN A GHOOST!

Apaart from ow Mrs. Wicks seein a ghoost – she see about one a week —thare hent bin a lot a-goin on in Dumpton.

We wor a-talkin about har an har ghoosts in tha Fox tha other night, an tha boy Chaarlie say "I wonder what them ghoosts dew when they ent bizzy harntin ow Mrs. Wicks?"

"Thass right," say Tom Drew tha landlord. "What dew,ghoosts dew when they're orf dewty?"

Ow Dan Forster, what set thare in tha corner, he let out a loud sniff. "They play snooker," he say.

Thet proper hulled us inter a buffle for a minnit, cos we'd forgotten Ow Dan wor thare.

"Play snooker?" say the boy Chaarlie in tha finish. "What, like Hurricane Higgins an all them what yew see on tha telly?"

"More or less," say Ow Dan. "If my troot wornt so dry, I could tell yer."

178

"Hare we go agin," say Tom Drew, fangin hold of Ow Dan's mug an fillin thet with mild.

* * *

"Thankyer," say Ow Dan, arter he'd swallered about haarf on it. "Well, like I wor a-sayin, thet wor when I wor a young un. Thare wor a billiard hall in Flitmarsh in them days, what wor pulled down when they built Woolwarth's.

"Let me see now, thet'd a bin jest arter tha fust warld war – no, hold yew on a minnit, thet wor jest afore tha war – or dew I tell a lie? My sister got married tha searme yare, so thet must a bin ... "

"Never yew mind about what yare thet wor," say Tom. "What happened?"

"Thass what I'm a-tellin on yer, ent it?" say Ow Dan. "Me an young Jeremiah Sparkes, we'd bin in thet thare billard hall all evenin, an then he went hoom, and I must a nodded orf in a corner. When tha feller in charge come round to lock up, he never see me.

"How long I wor asleep – I dornt know, but all of a sudden I wook up. An dew yew know what wook me?"

"Indigestion," say tha boy Chaarlie.

"Dornt talk sorft," say Ow Dan. "Thet wor tha sound o' balls a-clackin on them billiard tearbles. Proper put tha wind up me, thet did. I dussn't open my glimmers to start with, but when I did dew, I see all them tearbles smothered with snooker balls, an all them balls wor a-runnin about on their own, without nobodda wor a-hittin on em. Then I hud woices."

"Woices?" arst Fred Johnson.

* * *

"Ah," say Ow Dan, "woices. 'Thet wor a frewty ow shot, George,' say a woice right above my skull, alongside tha tearble next to whare I set.

" 'Oh no thet wornt, bor,' say some other woice. 'I played thet thare shot.'

" 'That yew never,' say the fust woice. 'Yew played tha pink inter the middle pocket, only thet missed, an went all round the tearble an inter tha bottom pocket orf o' the green. I tell yer, thet wor a proper fluke, or my nearme ent Albert Laarge.'

"I duzzy nare jumped clean out o' my chair," say Ow Dan, "when I hud the nearme Albert Laarge, cos Albert Laarge hed bin one o' tha best snooker players in the county till he fell off a hoss an got killed – oh, umpteen yares afore, if not more.

"Then stoon me if tha pink dint come a-searling up from under tha pocket an plarnt itself down on its spot.

" 'Alright then, George,' say the woice, 'let's see how yew git on with tha next red.'

"I set thare stammed as tha white ball went a-mizzlin down tha tearble torrards a red ball, missed it, an hit tha yeller.

" 'Foul strook!' I sung out. 'Fower away!'

* * *

"Well, my hart, thet done it. A duzzen diffrent woices all staarted a-hollerin at once, I felt myself being pulled out o' my chair, an a cue come an stuck itself in my hand.

" 'Come yew on then, ow paartner,' say tha woice what beloged to this hare feller called George, 'let's see if yew can beat Albert Laarge.'

"A frearme jumped on to tha tearble, all the reds rushed tew it an clustered inside it, an tha cullers sorted theirselves out on their spots. Afore I knew it, I wor a-playing a gearme o' snooker agin a feller what hed bin dead for yares."

"Did yew win?" arst the boy Chaarlie.

"I might a done," say Ow Dan, "only tha next thing I knew, thet wor daylight, an thare wornt nobodda a-playin snooker in thet thare billiard hall but me."

HARBERT
2nd October, 1981

DUMPTON DEFIANT STOPPED THA GEARME

Betwixt yew an me, we wor well on top in our gearme agin tha Church Lads when thet all ended in a shambles.

Fust go orf, Fred Johnson took a shot at goal what might a scored if tha goal-poosts hed bin a mile high. Tha ball went up like a rocket, hit a parssin crow, an come down agin in tha Wicar's gaarden. Thare wor a horrible sound o' brearkin glarss.

"Stoon me," I sung out, "thare go his cucumber frearmes agin."

Thass tha trouble with playin on tha Wicaridge medder. Thet dornt matters if thass football or cricket, no season ever go by without us gittin wrong with tha Wicar. I remember one time when a cricket ball went clean trew his study winder an come to rest on Foxe's Book o' Marters. My hart, he wor suffin riled.

"Never yew mind about fetchin tha ball back now," say tha ref, a squinty little feller called Biggs, what drive a milk van in Flitmarsh. "Yew can dew thet arterwards," he say, "we're got another what we can carry on with."

But we never carried on for much longer afore we see tha Wicar a-maarchin acrorst tha medder with tha ball under his aarm. Streart on to tha fild o' play he come, an streart up to tha ref, what blew his whissel an stopped tha gearme.

* * *

"Yew can pack this hare match in hare an now," say tha Wicar. "Thass tha umpteenth time my cucumber frearmes a bin smashed to bits."

"I carnt argew about thet now," say tha ref. "Thass a matter betwixt yew an tha club an tha insurance company, thet hent got narthin to dew with me."

"Thet will hev," say tha Wicar, "if yew dornt stop this hare match. Thass me what allow football to be played on tha Wicarage medder, an thass me whass got tha right to order tha footballers orf when they dammidge my property."

"Is thet a fack, Reverend," say Biggs. "Well let me tell yew suffin. Tha only one what a got a right to order footballers orf when a match is bein played is me. I can order tha publick orf o' tha pitch as well, so would yew kindly go an stand somewhare else till tha gearme finish, an then yew can argew about who pay for yar cucumber frearmes as much as what yew like."

I dornt rightly know who'd a won in tha finish, tha Wicar or Biggs, but neither one on em dint git no charnce to find out, cos jest then some o' tha spectearters, what hed bin a-hollerin "Tearke time orf, ref!" they started a-runnin in all direckshuns.

"Look behind yer!" shruck Enoch Fletcher, as he went parst me like a dorg arter a rabbit.

* * *

I slewed round, an stoon me if Ow Mother Quail's prize bull Dumpton Defiant, what come top o' his clarss in tha show t'yare, wornt a-lamperin acrorst tha medder with his skull haard down.

For one minnit I thowt he wor a-goin to come streart at me, but then he stopped an stood thare a-snortin.

Now what go on inside a bull's skull is beyond my know, but ow Dumpton Defiant looked to me like he wor imiteartin to mearke his mind up which on us'd give him tha best sport. Fust he took a squint this way, then he took a squint tha other, an in tha finish his ow glimmers lit on tha Wicar.

My hart, yew should a sin tha Wicar run, with Dumpton Defiant right behind him. I'll lay he hent never run so farst since he won a meddle in tha crorss-country at collidge, an thet must be tha best paart o' fifta yare ago. He dint stop to open his gearte, he jest dived clean over his hedge, an blow me if tha wornt another horrible sound o' brearkin glarss.

Thare wor a sound o' splinterin wood as well, cos tha ref hed shinnied up a goal-poost to git out o' tha bull's way, an when he put his weight on tha crorss-bar, thet brook.

* * *

One way an another, thet wor a rum ow job. Mind yew, ow George Wicks sune tarned up an led Dumpton Defiant away, but tha ref hed hed enoungh by then. Would he let us staart tha match agin? No, thet he woun't.

"Yew're hoom early, ent yer?" tha gal Alice say to me.

"Ah," I say. "Ow Mother Quail's bull come arter us."

"Lor," she say. "did he chaarge?"

"No, mor," I say, "he done it for narthin."

HARBERT
9th October, 1981

182

ALICE'S GARDEN

Tha trouble with tha gal Alice is, yew'd need a gaarden tha size of a football pitch to grow all tha things what she want yer to grow.

When she took a squint round our gaarden tha other mornin she say to me, she say: "Whare are all tha onions then?"

I say "Thass them thare, ent it?"

"My hart alive," she say, "thass a totty little ow onion bed, ent it? Yew know I use a lot o' onions when I'm a-cookin."

"We can git what more we want orf o' Chaarlie Baarley," I say. "Onions dew a lot better in his gaarden than what they dew in ours. He wor only a-sayin tha other night, dew we let him hev a bit o' our rhewbarb, he'll see us right when his onions are ready."

"I dornt see why we should give him any o' our rhewbarb," she say.

"Stoon me, mor," I say, "we're got more on it hare than what we can eat. We'd hatta be eatin stewed rhewbarb mornin, nune an night to git trew this lot"

"Not now I're got a freezer we on't," say tha gal Alice. "Whadda yew think I pestered yew to git me a freezer for? We can hev rhewbarb pies all next winter."

"I dint know yew could freeze rhewbarb," I say.

"Corse yew can," she say, "accordin to my freezer book. Yew pick thet when thass young an pink, yew warsh thet in cold runnin water, then yew cut thet up an freeze it. Thass sposed to larst a twelve-month in tha freezer."

* * *

"Well, mor," I say, "without we give ow Chaarlie Baarley some on it, we on't git none o' his onions."

"Thass a pity yew dint think o' thet afore," she say. "Thass tha searme with them roses."

I opened my gob to say suffin, but I shut thet agin right quick, cos I coun't see what them roses hed got to dew with them onions.

"Jest look at em," she say. "Thare's a good six or seven on em what on't come to narthin."

"Roses are like pearple," I say. "they dornt larst forever."

"They want to come out," she say. "I dornt want to see a lot o' dead rose bushes mearkin tha gaarden untidy."

"Some o' these hare ow roses a bin hare longer 'n what we hev," I say. "I'd a hed em up yares ago, only yew keep on a-hollerin yew want roses to put in yar vases."

"Thass right, put tha blearme on me," she say. "Thass allers tha woman's fault."

* * *

"Alright then, mor, I'll git rid on em," I say. "To tell yew tha trcwth, I'll be right glad to see tha back on em. So long as yew dornt go an tell me arterwards I dint oughter a done it."

"Dornt talk so sorft," she say. "Who want dead rose bushes in tha gaarden?"

I hed them ow rose bushes out in no time, an shifted a couple o' tha good uns round a bit. By tha time I'd done, I hed rume to sow a row o' carrots.

"Thare yew are then, mor," I say to tha gal Alice. "Are yew satisfied now?"

She screwed har fearce up tha way she dew when she git tha wrong chearnge from tha milkman.

"What a yew bin an done hare then?" she arst.

"I took them roses up like what yew wanted," I say.

"Ah," she say, "but yew're bin an put some seed in, hent yer?"

"Thass right," I say. "Carrots!"

"Carrots!" she shruck. "Whadda we want more carrots for? We're got tew rows up already. Besides, now we hent got no rume for tha roses."

"What roses?" I arst.

"Why, yew greart buzzlehid yew, tha new roses what go in whare them old roses come out," she say. "I dint tell yew to git rid o' them dead rose bushes so as yew could go an sow carrot seed. I thowt yew'd hev enough sense to git some o' them nice 'Peace' roses what they grow in pots from tha narsery at Fumbleham. Now I on't hev enough to cut for tha house."

"Stoon me, mor," I say, "yew'll want enough to put in tha freezer next."

HARBERT
30th April, 1982

BEN BEWGALL AND THA DIAMONDS - 1
Captin Hacksaw wor a-smugglin diamonds

THET must corst tha Fox money when ow Ben Bewgall spin us his yaarns about his life at sea, cos we all forgit to drink time he's a-talkin. On tha other hand, praps thass as broad as what thass long, cos ow Ben drink enough rum to kill a hoss. I'll lay he'd drunk tha best paart o' haarf a bottle by tha time he got to whare him an Tom Cooper an Rigger Smaart found out as how tha marster o' tha Southern Star, Captin Hacksaw Parkins, wor a-smugglin hoom diamonds inside an orstrich egg.

"He wor a crarfty ow devil when yew come to think on it," say ow Ben. "Pourin liquid glue trew tha hole in tha egg, an then droppin tha diamonds in on top on it so as they'd stick farst an woun't rattle.

"'We ent a-goin to let him git away with it, are we, Ben?' say Rigger.

"'Not if I can help it,' I say. 'I're hed tha shaarp edge o' his tongue more times than what I can remember. so he ent no friend o' mine.'

*   *   *

"'I reckon we desarve them diamonds more than what he dew,' say Tom. 'I know a widder in Yarmouth what could dew with a few.'

"'Fust thet wor a widder in Limehouse, then thet wor a widder in Wapping, an now thass a widder in Yarmouth.' I say. 'Yew're got thet many widders in tow, bor, yew on't never hev enough diamonds to go round.'

" 'Never mind about Tom's widders,' say Rigger. 'What I want to know is, how are we a-goin to mearke ow Hacksaw an them diamonds paart company?'

"'Easy,' say Tom, what wor allers a hearsty sort o' feller. 'We jest nip in an nick em when he ent about.'

"'Dornt talk so sorft, Tom,' I say. 'Tha minnit he miss em he'll sarch tha ship from stem to starn, an then whare'll we be?'

"'What we'll hatta dew,' say Rigger, 'is stuff another egg with them cheap glarss beads what look like diamonds, an then swop it for tha one in his cabin so as he on't know tha diffrence. Like thet thare, he on't never find out till he git hoom, an by thet time we'll a signed orf an be miles away.'

"'Thass tha best plan alright,' I say. 'But thet want a bit o' thinkin about. Thet ent as easy as what thet sound.' "

* * *

"'I dornt see why not,' say Tom. 'Yew know thet thare ostrich faarm whare we went, an tha feller in chaarge wor pleased to see us an give us them feathers? Well, blow me, if we went back he'd let us hev an egg.'

"'So he might,' I say, 'but thet ent jest an egg what we want. Thass an egg whass tha searme size an culler as ow Hacksaw's egg. All them eggs are slightly diffrent.'

"'What we'll hatta dew then,' say Rigger, 'is weart till ow Hacksaw hev bisness ashore what we know will keep him away for a day an a night, then we'll hatta nick his egg, an then we'll hatta breark inter tha orstrich faarm arter daark an nick one o' their eggs.'

"'Apaart from all thet,' I say, 'we'll hatta find some shops whare we can buy some liquid glue an glarss beads, an drill a hole in tha egg tha exack size o' tha one in Hacksaw's egg, an git tha innards out, an shove tha glue an tha beads in, an git a pair o' scales from somewhere so as we can weigh booth… .

"'Stoon me,' say Tom, 'is thet all?'

"Tha more we thowt about it, tha trickier thet fared to sound. But tha nexter mornin Rigger come a-rushin up an say, 'Hev yew hud? Ow Hacksaw's gorn ashore an on't be back till tomorrer.'

"'Shipmeartes,' I say, 'now's our charnce.'"

HARBERT
10th September 1982
(Continued next week)

BEN BEWGALL AND THA DIAMONDS - 2
Tha plot is hatched

ARTER ow Ben Bewgall hed swallered a bit more rum, he got on with his yaarn about them thare diamonds what Hacksaw Parkins, tha marster o' tha Southern Star, hed hid inside an orstrich egg.

"Once ow Hacksaw wor out o' tha way," he say, "me an Tom Cooper an Rigger Smaart swung inter ackshun.

"Nickin thet thare egg out o' his cabin never give us no trouble. Rigger Smaart, what come of a long line o' crooks, he could a brook inter tha Bank o' England with a hairpin, he could, so he wor inter Hacksaw's cabin an out agin in a flash, with tha egg stuffed up his garnsey.

"What did give us trouble wor gittin another egg all ready to leave in its plearce. Like I told yer, our plan wor to nick an egg from tha orstrich faarm, pour glue in it, drop some glarss beads in on top, an then shove it in Hacksaw's cabin so as he woun't know no different.

"'This hare's a-goin to corst us a mint o' money afore we're done.' I say, as I nipped inter an ironmonger's.

"'Git away,' say Tom , 'bit o' glue on't cost a lot.'

"'Thet ent only glue we want in this hare shop,' I say, 'thass a drill.'

"'Ben's right,' say Rigger. 'We're gotta drill a hole in tha egg, hent we?'"

* * *

"'I never thowt o' thet,' say Tom. 'When we wor kids, we used to prick booth ends of a bud's egg with a pin, dint we, an then blow it.'

"'Stoon me,' I say, 'thass an orstrich egg what we're a-dealin with now, not a blooming doddy-wren's egg. They're got shells as thick as dinner-pleartes, them ostrich eggs hev, an twice as haard.'

"'Besides which,' say Rigger, 'we'll hatter mearke sartain tha hole in our egg's tha searme size as tha hole in Hacksaw's, else he might git suspicious.'

"'I reckon what'll corst us tha moost money,' I say, 'is a weighin machine. When we're done with it, our egg a gotta weigh tha searme as ow Hacksaw's, right down to tha larst frackshun of an ounce.'

"I wor right an all – tha weighin mashine corst us a duzzy forchune. We got one o' them sort with a tray on top an a dial to one side, like what wimmen use nowadays in kitchens.

"Then we nipped out o' sight up an alley an weighed ow Hacksaw's egg, an I writ down tha weight on a bit o' pearper.

"'Alright then, shipmeartes,' I say, 'our next stop's tha butcher's.'

"'What tha hike dew we want at tha butcher's?' arst Tom.

"'Meat for tha dorgs,' I say.

"'What dorgs?' arst Tom.

"'I see what Ben's a-gittin at,' say Rigger. 'There'll be dorgs a-prowlin round thet thare orstrich faarm at night. Without we hull em a lump o' meat to keep em quiet, we'll be done.'

"'An we'd best stuff suffin in tha meat to send em to sleep,' I say. 'Yew're tha expart, Rigger. I're sin yew drop things in feller's drinks afore today. Dew yew hop down tew tha chemist's an git whatever yew need.'

"'Right yew are, bor, say Rigger. 'An time I'm down tha chemists, yew'd best slip back to tha ironmonger's.'

"'What for?' I arst.

"'Why, bor,' say Rigger. 'I dorn't see how we're a-goin to git tha innards out o' thet thare egg without we hev some sort o' pump.'"

* * *

"I tell yer, by tha time we'd bin round all tha shops, an got some glarss beads, an a brearce an bit, an them kitchen scearles, an a pump, an meat for tha dorgs, an glue, an stuff from tha chemist's an I dornt know what else, we dint haardly hev enough money left for a pint apiece.

"'Never yew fret,' I say, as we wet our troots, 'yew'red gotta spend money to mearke money in this life, an when yew think o' all them diamonds in thet thare egg up Rigger's garnsey, I reckon yew can call this hare equipment a good inwestment.'

"So then we drunk up an maarched orf to breark inter tha orstrich faarm."

HARBERT
17th September 1982
(More next week)

BEN BEWGALL AND THA DIAMONDS - 3
An orstrich egg warth £100,000

What sort o' duller orstriches kick up is beyond my know, but if they're anything like geese, I reckon thet'd be enough to deafen yer. Leastways, thass what I wor a-thinkin as ow Ben Bewgall telled us how him an Tom Cooper an Rigger Smaart brook inter tha orstrich faarm.

But accordin to ow Ben, them orstriches wor as quiet as mice. "Thet wor proper uncanny," he say. "Talk about silence – thet wor more like a grearveyaard than an orstrich faarm. Even tha ow dorgs never baarked. They jest come a-mifflin round cos they could smell tha meat what we'd got for em. An once they'd hed some o' tha meat, they rolled over an went to sleep. I dornt know what Rigger put in thet thare meat, but my hart if thet dint wark quick.

"We mearde our way to tha greart ow shud whare tha eggs wor kept for hatchin. Thet wor locked, o' corse, but locks wornt never no problem for Rigger.

"So thare we stood on what I might call tha brink o' success – an thare wornt no eggs in sight.

" 'They're all in them incubearters I reckon,' say Tom.

" 'Let's hoop they hent set yit then,' I say, 'else thet'll be marder gittin tha innards out trew a hole in tha shell.'

"Well, we opened them incubearters, one arter tha other, till we found an egg to sewt our parpose.

"Rigger hed ow Hacksaw Parkins's egg with tha diamonds in it stuffed up his garnsey, so he whipped thet out an we measured them eggs agin one another. They wor a parfick match.

"We dint hang about arter thet, I can tell yer. We run back to tha Southern Star, egg an all, as farst as what we could go.

" 'Well, thass tha warst paart over,' I say, as we nipped inter tha pearnt locker out o' sight.

"Mind yew, I wor wrong. Brearkin inter tha orstrich faarm an nickin thet thare egg wor child's play compared to what come next. Cos what come next wor tha job o' fixin thet thare egg up so as when we put thet in ow Hacksaw's cabin he coun't tell tha diffrence.

* * *

"I dornt know if yew're ever imitearted to drill a hole in an orstrich egg with a brearce an bit. All I can say is, thass a rum ow job. Dew yew tearke my adwice – if yew're a-sarnterin along tha cliffs at Cromer, or acrorst tha maarshes at Hickling, an yew charnce to see an orstrich egg lay thare, dew yew walk right parst an pay no regaard tew it.

"Howsomever, we got thet all done in tha finish. We got tha shell cleaned out, poured in tha glue, then stuck tha egg on our weighin mashine and dropped in tha glarss beads till thet weighed exackly what thet wor sposed to weigh.

"Arter thet, Rigger went an left it in Hacksaw's cabin, an tha job wor done.

" 'Shipmeartes,' I say, 'we're rich. When ow Hacksaw come back tomorrer, he'll think he're still got an egg full o' diamonds, on't he. But he on't hev, will he, cos we're got tha one with tha diamonds in, hent we. So let's hev a squint at it, Rigger, an see if we can mearke out how rich we are.'

"Rigger stood thare stammed.

" 'I hent got it,' he say. Tom's got it.'

" 'Thet I hent,' say Tom.

" 'Thet yew hev,' say Rigger. 'I give thet to yew to hold time we wor a-puttin them eggs back in them incubearters.'

" 'Thet yew never,' say Tom.

"To cut a long story short," say ow Ben, a-fillin his glarss up with rum for tha larst time, " thet tarned out as how Tom hed bin an mixed our egg up with all them other eggs.

"We hed a miserable woyage hoom, I can tell yer.

"An when we see a report in tha newspearpers, we could a howled. All about a scientifick mistry in South America – an orstrich egg what hatched out diamonds instead of an orstrich – hed tha orstrich what laid it bin a-pickin up diamonds an a-swallerin on em?

"But tha bit what mearde us hull Tom in tha harber wor whare tha newspearper reckoned thet thare egg wor warth £100,000."

HARBERT
24th September 1982

THA CASE WAS FLAWED

Ow Mr Lucas Miffler, tha chairman o' tha Bench, he took one squint at tha chaarge-sheet an he say: "We hent got narthin sarious hare this morning."

"An a good job tew," say Elijah Frogg, him what they call Fresher. "I're got stock to tend tew when I git hoom."

"I want to git away quick myself," say Buncombe tha corn marchant.

"Narthin sarious. did yew say, Mr Miffler?" arst little Miss Crimp, what set thare like a sparrer with a black hat on.

"Thass right, ma'am, narthin serious," say Mr Miffler. "Only some woman whass chaarged with nickin some other woman's teapot."

Up sprung a long, thin feller in a daark grey sewt, what we all reckernised as Mr Jellicoe Hickey, o' Stott an Hickey, tha well-known sollisiters.

"May thet please yar warships," he say, "thare may be more in this hare cairse than what meet tha eye. Accordin tew tha walue plearced upon tha teapot by its owner, thass warth hundreds if not thousans. She reckon thet ent no ordinry teapot."

"Well I go to jail," say ow Mr Miffler. "Let me see now – how much is thet down for in tha chaarge?"

"We coun't put a price on it," say Inspeckter Churkey. "Not without expart adwice we coun't. Thass why thass down on tha chaarge-sheet as a teapot of considerable, but unsartain walue."

"Exackly, yar warships," say Mr Hickey. "An thet, I respeckfully submit, is whare tha police a mearde a sarious error, cos tha teapot what my client is alleged to hev nicked – I beg yar paarden, stolen – ent warth fowerpence."

"Tha owner will dispute thet when she come to tha witness box, yar warships," say Inspeckter Churkey. "She say thet belonged to har greart-granmother's granmother. She say thet wor mearde to maark Queen Wictoria's coronearshun, so thet must be warth a bomb on tha anteeks maarket."

* * *

In come Mrs Caroline Muffin, what pleaded not gilty, an Mrs Brenda Broom, what telled tha Bench har teapot wor priceless.

"I submit," say Mr Hickey for tha defence, "as how tha teapot in

191

question ent narthin more than a common teapot like what yew can find in tha shops, exceptin thet it dew hev 'A Present from Yarmouth' writ on it."

"An a pickcher o' Queen Wictoria's hid as well," sung out Mrs Broom, what looked like she could knock ow Hickey's skull orf dew she got haarf a charnce.

"Keep yew yar wool on, missis," say Mr Miffler. "Yew're hed yar tarn to speak."

"I'm much obliged to yar warship," say Mr Hickey. "I agree as how some woman's hid dew form paart o' tha decorearshun on tha teapot, but thet dornt look much like Queen Wictoria to me, nor any other queen for thet matter. May I respeckfully remind yar warships…"

"Hold yew yar hosses a minnit, Mr Stickey," say Mr Miffler, "time tha Bench examine tha exhibit. We sharnt git no forrarder without we tearke a good squint at it."

They give ow Buncombe tha teapot, an he stuck his snout in it.

"What dew thet look like to yew then, Buncombe?" arst Mr Miffler.

Ow Buncombe scratched his skull.

* * *

"In my expart opinion," say Buncombe, "thet jest fare to look like a teapot – narthin more, narthin less."

"I tell yew thass historick!" shruck Mrs Broom, goin red in tha fearce. "Thass why thet thare mucky-fearced Caroline Muffin went an nicked thet orf of me. Thass warth thousans!"

By this time little Miss Crimp hed tha teapot in har hands.

"I dornt know if thet might a bin warth thousans at one time," she say, "but thet ent warth much now, cos thass liable to fall to bits at any minnit. Thare's a laarge crack right round it."

Mrs Broom went shanny.

"What!" she hollered. "My teapot cracked! Then tha police must a done it. I demarnd compensearshun! I'll sue tha police force! Tha Hoom Secketary'll hatta dew suffin about this hare!"

She wor still a-hollerin when I left, so I carnt tell yer how ow Miffler sorted thet one out.

HARBERT
9th February, 1989